WITHDRAWN
University Libraries
University of Memphis

3

MAIN LIBR
DATE DUE
02 5.92

Better Report Writing

Second Edition, Revised and Enlarged

WILLIS H. WALDO

New York

REINHOLD PUBLISHING CORPORATION

Chapman & Hall, Ltd., London

Copyright © 1965 by

REINHOLD PUBLISHING CORPORATION

All rights reserved

Library of Congress Catalog Card Number: 65-27325
Printed in the United States of America

Copy 3

PE
1478
W3
1965
Copy 3

4110110

Except ye utter . . . words easy to be understood, how shall it be known what is spoken?

I Cor. 14:9

Preface

The important quotation below appears in a report issued in 1963 commonly called the Weinberg Report.*

"Much more obvious than any deficiency in our understanding of the communication process itself, or in the possible application of journalistic techniques, is our inability to use natural English properly. This Panel is gravely concerned, as are many others who have written on the information problem, that so many American scientists and technologists can neither speak nor write effective English, that the new language of science and technology is turgid, heavy and unclear."

The purpose of this book is to help to correct this situation. Some chapters are devoted to rules of grammar and punctuation, but rules are not enough. The kind of subject matter to which an author applies these rules is just as important.

It is up to him to write more effectively and persuasively. That, and not the rules, is the important thing. A scientist who feels strongly about his research and the work he has done will want to describe it well.

There is magic in words. The unique excitement of saying and writing exactly what he means, forcefully and effectively, can be felt by a technical report writer.

The thrill in conquering a reader with his report can be experienced by a scientist. It is not so hard to accomplish if the writer attacks his technical report with enthusiasm, sparkling words, and empathy for his reader.

I have been concerned with technical information problems for nearly two decades. During this time much progress has been made in retrieving

* "Science, Government, and Information," a report of the President's Advisory Committee, January 10, 1963, available from the U.S. Superintendent of Documents, Washington 25, D.C., 25 cents.

data, information, documents, and references from a storehouse. Concurrently, the storehouse has been filling rapidly with timeless data and information stored in documents with "turgid, heavy, and unclear" English.

Dr. Harold Urey, on the occasion of the successful landing of Ranger 8 on the moon, February 20, 1965, was asked whether the scientific information gained by the moon shot was worth the expense. He replied, "I do not know what a scientific fact is worth." If, in the opinion of the experimenter, it was worth the cost of obtaining, it is surely worth the same enthusiasm, care, and thoughtfulness to store it in a document worthy of the cost of our advances in retrieval.

Credit for this completely revised edition should go to my wife, Anna Lee, who, except for her wishes, would be a coauthor, and to G. G. Hawley of Reinhold Publishing Corporation, whose enthusiasm and urgings gave me the impetus to continue as an author.

W. H. W.

Kirkwood, Missouri
September, 1965

Contents

Contents

CHAPTER 1 *Principal Principles*

One product of research is information, and the written word is one means by which this product is transmitted for use. Writing is a key part of research activities, and its quality is a vital force.

Writing is either hard or easy, as the author makes it. For most persons who have not written very much, the chief difficulty is uncertainty as to what should be done first. Worrying about this and related questions often takes more out of the new author than work itself.

What should the title be?

Should I use all these illustrations or none?

What is a good opening sentence?

How many copies should I make?

He tries to see the completely finished paper at the very start— perhaps even before he has gathered and organized the material. At that stage he cannot even worry intelligently about the paper, much less see his way to working on it usefully.

Writing a paper or report is work, and it should be undertaken in a workmanlike manner. There is no mystery about it. There is a definite series of steps to completing a writing job. Each step has its characteristic problems and makes its contribution to the finished paper. The beginning of wisdom in writing, and of freedom from worry, is in seeing these various stages clearly so that each can be attacked by itself and the paper advanced in an orderly and profitable fashion.

Technical information reported logically, accurately, and neatly will command the interest and respect of readers. Material reported carelessly will not. It behooves the author to present his work in as good form as possible, because this is his "brag sheet."

Report writing as a form of communication may be divided into seven consecutive steps:

(1) Gaining an understanding of the objectives, of the existing situation, and of the needs of the specific readers of the report.

(2) Gathering and organizing the facts and information.

(3) Analyzing the assembled data to the extent that proper solutions, convictions, applications, conclusions, and recommendations may be reached.

(4) Writing the rough draft.

(5) Checking, revising, rearranging, and rewriting the draft.

(6) Reviewing for arrangement, style, mechanics, and distribution.

(7) Typing in final form, proofreading, duplicating, assembling, binding, and distributing.

The purpose of a report is to answer a question. Perhaps the question is put to the author by someone else. Perhaps the author anticipates that someone will put it to him. Or perhaps the question arises in the author's mind. In any event, here is where the report must open—with the question.

State the question. Even the reader closest to the work may not remember the question, so he needs a review, a reminder, or orientation. The author must define the question, and he must limit its scope. Scarcely anything is more irritating to a busy man than to read a lot of facts without knowing what they are all about, without first having been oriented.

The writer must also explain promptly why the question has arisen. Perhaps equipment has failed or is giving trouble. Maybe something will do better than the old equipment. Of course he should say so, but he should start at the beginning and tell what the old equipment does. He should be sure his reader can start with him and should give enough information so that the reader will be able to follow him all the way through the report.

Reports are seldom acted upon quickly. Although they may be read promptly, they may be put aside for months or even years before finances or other conditions will permit action. The author must always keep the delayed user in mind when he writes a report. He must pay attention to the effect of time on his words.

If the author is confident of his objectives, knows the present situation, and understands the needs of his readers, he may reasonably begin to assemble his facts and information for organizing. This organizing will take by far the largest part of the time required for the report. Some scientific and scholarly works may represent accumulations of a lifetime. This stage of assembly is often neglected by the hurried or inexperienced author.

If he wonders why he has trouble writing his paper, the answer may be the simple truth that he hasn't accumulated enough detailed material to write a coherent story.

"Whatever we conceive well we express clearly," said Boileau-Despreaux, a French writer. If engineers and scientists have a good, clear concept of the meaning of their work, they are a long way on the road to expressing their findings clearly. The author can double or triple the effectiveness of his writing by carefully isolating the facts most useful to his reader and presenting these first.

Here are some helpful guides to selecting and presenting facts: (1) Every time an author finds it necessary to describe either a simple or intricate process, experiment, procedure, etc., he should extract from this the main facts. He should set these aside for presentation in the introduction. Thus, for a process, he might isolate the production rate, units per hour, and unit cost. For an experiment he might isolate the ease of performance and the reliability of the results. In discussing a procedure he could cite its usefulness in detecting certain important information. (2) The author should usually present results, findings, and conclusions first, and follow these with his evidence. (3) He should key his results, findings, and conclusions to his probable reader, emphasizing items of greatest interest to the reader. (4) He should be brief— and not try to impress the reader with the depth of his knowledge. In general, the briefer his written items are, the more forceful they will be, if his information is carefully chosen. Reading technical reports is work; the author must make it easier by being concise and accurate.

Material comes from memory, from observation and experiment, from talking with colleagues, from reading, studying, reasoning and speculation. The writer's chief distinction often comes from the small bits of information which he has to report. The interest and value of many reports depend on the amount of first-hand detail they contain. The writer's own opinions, hypotheses, and generalizations are evolved (often during the actual writing process) by examining and comparing and reflecting on the data he has gathered. Little of importance can be written without some author speculation on the facts presented.

S. I. Hayakawa, editor of the small, but stimulating quarterly magazine *ETC: A Review of General Semantics* wrote, "The distinction between observed facts and opinions or conclusions about them—or, in written and spoken language, between reports and judgments—is one that is very easy to overlook. Are you aware of the difference between your remarks, 'He's a swell guy!' and 'He loaned me five dollars'? Of the difference between 'The cost of living is too high' and 'My living expenses have doubled in the past four years, while my salary has gone up 50 percent in the same period'?"

Report writers must adhere to the following rules: (1) Their facts must be capable of verification. (2) They must exclude, as far as possible, inferences and judgments in the presentation of data.

The author may not always be able to verify all the facts in his report, but if he and his readers agree on the names of things, on what constitutes a "gram," "foot," "decibel," and how to measure time, there is relatively little danger of misunderstanding. Even in a world such as we have today, in which everybody seems to be quarreling with everybody else, we still, to a surprising degree, trust one another's reports. We read books about science, mathematics, automotive engineering, geography, travel, and other such factual matters, and we usually assume that the author is doing his best to tell us what he knows as truly as he can. We are safe in so assuming most of the time. With the emphasis that is being given today to the discussion of biased newspapers, propagandists, and the general untrustworthiness of many of the communications we receive, we are likely to forget that we still have an enormous amount of reliable information available and that deliberate mis-information in technical fields is still more the exception than the rule. The desire for self-preservation that compelled men to evolve means for the exchange of information also compels them to regard the giving of false information as profoundly reprehensible.

At its highest development, the language of reports is the language of science. By "highest development" is meant general usefulness. All literate peoples, no matter what race, religion, political affiliation, or vocation, agree on the meaning of such symbols as:

$$2 + 2 = 4; \ 100°C; \ H_2SO_4; \ 3{:}45 \ \text{p.m.};$$

$$x = \frac{-b \pm \sqrt{b^2 - 4ac}}{2a} \ ; \ \sum_{n=1}^{\infty} (-1)^n; \ \int_C f(z)dz, \text{ etc.}$$

The language of reports, then, including the more accurate reports of science, is "map" language, and because it gives us reasonably accurate representations of the "territory," it enables us to get work done.

An author will find that practice in writing reports is a quick means of increasing his linguistic awareness. Reports are generally about firsthand experience—things the reader has done himself. They should be of such a nature that they can be verified and agreed upon.

Observations and inferences drawn from these observations must be clear-cut. The common characteristic of inferences is that they are statements about matters which are not directly known, made on the basis of what has been observed. Some reports require the author to make an inference. For instance, the author may infer from a halo on an unexposed photographic plate that it has been in the vicinity of radioactive materials, or he may infer from the character of the ruins the origin of the fire that destroyed the building. An author must not make careless inferences. For example, the inferences a good mechanic can make about the internal condition of a motor by listening to it are often startlingly accurate, while the inferences made by an amateur often are entirely wrong—if he even tries to make any.

In a report, judgments are the expressions of the author's approval or disapproval of the occurrences, or objects he is describing. It is better for an author to say, for example, "This car was driven 60,000 miles and has never required any repairs" before he makes a judgment and says, "It is a fine car." Scientific verifiability rests upon the external observation of facts, not upon the heaping up of judgments.

In a technical report inferences and judgments belong to the part of the body termed "Discussion."

By being aware of favorable or unfavorable feelings that certain words and facts can arouse, the author can attain enough impartiality for practical purposes. This awareness enables the author to balance the implied favorable and unfavorable judgments against each other.

Implied Favorable	Unfavorable
Forty percent are still living.	Sixty percent died during the first year.
The reaction was irreversible.	
The product was white, hexagonal crystals.	The reaction took 28 hrs. to complete. The product came in a 9 percent yield.

This process of selecting details favorable or unfavorable to the report may be termed slanting. Slanting gives no explicit judgments, but it differs from objective reporting in that it deliberately makes certain judgments inescapable. The author striving for impartiality will, therefore, take care to slant both for and against his subject, trying as conscientiously as he can to keep the balance even. For example:

After five years 40% of the patients are still living, although 60% died during the first year of treatment.
The reaction took 28 hrs. to complete, but it was not reversible.
The product was obtained in only a 9% yield, but the white, hexagonal crystals were pure.

A few weeks of practice in writing reports, slanted reports, and reports slanted both ways will improve powers of observation, as well as ability to recognize soundness of observation in the writings of others. A sharpened sense for the distinction between facts and judgments, facts and inferences, will reduce susceptibility to the flurries of frenzied public opinion which certain authors or reporters find it to their interest to arouse. Alarming judgments and inferences can be made to appear inevitable by means of skillfully slanted reports. An author (and reader) who is aware of the technique of slanting, however, is relatively difficult to stampede by such methods. He knows too well that there may be other relevant facts which have been left out.*

The importance of trying to "slant both ways" does not lie in the hope of achieving an impartiality in one's own thinking and writing—manifestly an impossible goal. It lies in discovering what poor authors of reports most of us really are, and how little we see of the world since we of necessity see it from our own point of view. To discover one's own biases is the beginning of wisdom.

The time for an author to start preparing a report is before the project is started. He should constantly keep in mind that a report is to be written. Preliminary writing can be done as the work progresses.

A fertile, active mind is continually ahead of the physical conditions surrounding it. As the laboratory work is being done, a competent worker finds himself speculating, testing, and rejecting with variations on what he is doing. Occasionally something solid occurs to him. If this thought upon reflection is worthy, it is recorded either by memory or in a lab notebook for testing at a later date. This thinking operation, since it is highly personal, has three attributes; it's sincere, it's prompt, and it's clear.

Report writing should be embodied thought. There are three principles involved in conveying thoughts to readers. These principles are the same as the attributes in contemplative thinking.

(1) Never lie to the reader.
(2) Inform as promptly as possible.
(3) Be sure communication is complete.

If authors succeed in applying these principles properly, readers become eager to know more. Failure to tell an honest story promptly and completely, on the other hand, invites a cynical attitude. The reader cries, "Pious platitudes; a jungle of jargon."

For a broader discussion on preparing to write, read "Think Before You Write." †

* See discussion of slanted definitions in Chapter 11.

† Leary, W. G. and Smith, J. S., Harcourt, Brace and Co., New York, 1951.

CHAPTER 2 *Emphasis on Empathy*

The reader's confidence in the writer is an unseen but real aid to communication. The writer's projection into the needs of the reader is the basis for this confidence.

If you ignore the interests of the reader, you can expect the report to be ignored. Imagine the reader's environment, education, information needs, and build his confidence. A writer begins to communicate when he has gained the reader's confidence. He does this by placing emphasis on empathy for the people whom he expects to be his report readers: he must train himself to appreciate *their* needs and *their* viewpoints.

The writer must give careful thought to the identity of the readers. There are many barriers inherent in a reading audience that can prevent a message from getting through to the proper people. The "state of knowledge" that the readers hold is one important barrier. At the moment an author decides that he has found sufficient information to compose a report, he knows something about the specific problem at hand that no one else does. An important function of his report is that of a teacher, and all his readers, for awhile, become his students. Since there will never be an opportunity for a formal placement examination, each author must approximate what grade his students will make. The sophistication and language in various parts of the report should reflect the hypothetical grades the author has given to his students, the readers.

What is the situation in many American colleges today which, in the interest of being known as a progressive school with an appreciation of what employers look for in their graduates, have introduced courses in report writing? It is generally true that most college English teachers are well trained specialists with rather highly specialized interests. These interests are largely literature and language; the specialties may be in literary appreciation, literary history, literary scholarship, or philology. None of these special interests is shared by any great number of the general students or even those who find their way into the college English classroom. Yet English—one of the few subjects almost universally required of college students—is taught almost exclusively by such specialists.

It is from this group of academic specialists that teachers of technical writing are chosen. In most cases, from a very pragmatic sense, no better choice is available to the curriculum administrator.

If the students taking report writing are advanced students—and this is usually the case—they are gradually gaining a specialty of their own, although at that time it may be somewhat broad. It is not inconceivable,, however, that a medical student might write a report in such a course on "Stabilizing Actions of Adenosine Triphosphate and Related Nucleotides on Calcium-Deficient Nerve," or that an engineering student might do some literature search and write a report on "Double Horizontal Capstan Winch," or that a chemistry student might write about "The Nature of Gamma Radiation."

It is apparent that this interrelationship of specialists creates a gap in empathy—one that is practically unbridgeable. And so the student must learn early that he must write for his reader, the instructor. He must write in such a manner that the English instructor has a pretty good idea what is meant by a calcium-deficient nerve, a particular type of winch, or gamma radiation. The student must try to bridge the gap.

Because he is a teacher and interested in his students' progress, the instructor must try to understand what the student's technical interests are. By the end of the course, if the students in report writing have learned to present topics in which they are interested in such a way that their instructor in report writing has learned something of the technical interests of his students, then the teacher has been successful.

The initiative in bridging the gap in empathy between the specialized English teacher and the student of technical writing, of course, belongs with the teacher. If the student has not learned, the teacher has not taught. The teacher must succeed in presenting an understanding of the problems of syntax; he must make clear the intricacies of synonyms; he must have pointed out the pitfalls of semantics; but above all he should put his emphasis on empathy. And a writer who ignores the interests of his readers deserves the anonymity which he will achieve.

Alexander Gode, the Father of Interlingua, is credited with the most thwarting commentary on mediocre writing: "I understand you perfectly well, but I do not know what you mean."

After he has left the classroom, a report writer is likely to find three classes of readers. First are the executives, interested only in the status, significance, conclusions, or recommendations of a report. There are others who may wish to know why the general conclusions are drawn—something about the parts that make up the whole. Finally, there are people who must check detail, such as the lab men, even to repeating the work at a later date. These three classes may be represented by many different people. Each has a right to the author's empathy and attention.

Many engineers and scientists hide their main findings or conclusions under layers of abstruse technical information. As a result, the reader becomes mired in a mass of information he can't use, hardly understands, and dislikes reading. The reader tosses the written piece aside. He loses because he obtains only a small part of the information he sought. The author of the piece also loses because only a portion of his message is understood by his readers. The author can learn to write grammatically and to spell correctly. All he needs is a dictionary. Punctuation can be improved—there are many fine books available. The most handy is a copy of a Merriam-Webster's dictionary. But organization of technical and scientific material takes skill. It requires (1) a knowledge of the subject, and (2) a grouping of information and facts to best serve the reader.

The author already has a knowledge of his field. With a little study he can learn to recognize his reader's interests and needs. Combining these two—knowledge and recognition—he can group his data to best serve his reader.

The author has an obligation, acknowledged by many devoted teachers, to recognize his students as humans with limitations. More important, these humans have individual rights and personalities. No successful teacher exposes a feeling of superiority to his students. Report writers must also recognize that their audience is not captive. To get and hold the attention of his readers is simply a form of good manners. The author who shows courtesy to his reader by taking pains to present his material interestingly, warmly, and with some dignified color can feel rewarded because he won and held the concentration of his readers. The increasing competition for attention requires that the successful author will be the one who adds *sparkle* to his report.

Authors are people, and as such are often guilty of two well known sins. The first is laziness; the second is fear.

No one can learn the art of writing by reading this book. Those who care to improve may find help by reading on. Those who have problems in writing may discover answers through their reading. Better reports, however, come only by applying these answers to actual reports. Skilled technical writing is the product of many hours or even many years in writing, self-criticism, rewriting, and maintaining the incentive to improve.

Technical authors show laziness in many ways. There are few organizations that get reports written without a considerable amount of cajoling, and often threats. When the report shows up for typing, it is abominably scribbled, full of fantastically conceived abbreviations, misspelled words, poor grammar and punctuation, and is often crudely thrown together. If the author is asked to proofread his own report after typing or composing, he does so only out of courtesy. Few authors have the interest to examine a document critically for errors. Proofreading is hard mental effort and requires an attention discipline seldom evident in technical authors.

No greater indictment of the laziness of authors has been levied than the recent enthusiastic reception ghost writing has received. Ghost writing of reports is taking away from scientists the responsibility of accounting for their laboratory creations.

Although laziness may have the technical author chained, fear has him paralyzed. The absence of positive statements in reports has become a universal criticism. Why? Aristotle had the answer, "It is because there is less opportunity of error in generalities that soothsayers express themselves in general terms of their subject."

The authors' fear of their readers is nearly universal. Evidence is the absence of positive statements in technical reports.

Wave lengths *tentatively* assigned are *thought* to have a *probable* error of *less* than 0.02 Å.

This tenuous statement is a true example of the fear of criticism found in technical communications in the *exact* science of physics.

Those who seem to know exclaim that more basic, fundamental research is sorely needed in this country. One answer may be that there are few scientists bold enough to publish any discovery that is really new because they remember with fear in their hearts the beating that phlogiston took and the laugh that universal ether received. They are so afraid of being wrong that they essay nothing. They have no faith in their own scientific observations.

Another answer may be that the reviewers and editors of the current technical journals also fear criticism because they have dared to publish something completely new and different. They are afraid that their contemporaries will brand their particular journal as extreme. They form a great society of conformists—these timorous authors, editors, and reviewers.

Too often writers turn to the technical journals to find out how a report ought to be done. Indeed their peers and supervisors have advised this. The authors of papers published in technical journals are just as scared as the report writers. It is true that there are editors of journals; but these editors are beset with problems they deem more important than quality writing. They must reject eighty percent of their papers because of space limitation. They must not injure the feelings of an eminent author who has been appointed to the editorial board.

The referee system should keep high the quality of writing in scientific journals. But referees are too likely to be concerned with the impact of the new ideas on their own research, instead of deciding whether the paper carries ideas already published and conforming to highly specialized rules for that particular journal.

Editors and referees, of course, must do these things. A well-written paper containing questionable conclusions should certainly not be published simply because it is well written. If all the papers submitted to a journal were accepted for publication subject only to the author revitalizing the writing, many journals would simply go broke, because of the glut of submittals.

Using the journals, nevertheless, as a guide to writing is inbreeding the faults of the past rather than trying to improve. Too many papers appear in journals written by men whose professional future is related to the number of their publications. Language can show you are a professional; but report writing is a communications medium, not a status symbol.

If those who call themselves scientists would eschew laziness and fear, they would soon find that their ineptness in writing would disappear and our technical journals, industrial, and academic reports would improve in quality.

But authors and editors are not solely responsible for the poor shape of technical communications. Before a telephone communication system is complete, the listener must lift the phone and then must listen to the communicator.

Report readers in industrial management have only begun to provide realistic reporting systems. Many systems are as archaic and inefficient as the rural party-line telephone system. Such systems distribute reports to all types of reader. But the busy executive says reports are too long and the co-worker scientist says that they do not give sufficient details.

There is too much jargon for the general reader; the specialized reader insists on the presence of jargon which belongs to his particular field. The pull-and-haul instructions given authors are enough to throw fear into an Albert Einstein.

Well-meaning executives often fail to practice what they preach in their attempts to instruct report writers. How frequently have you heard these words: "Avoid vague statements—be clear and concise."

The truth of the matter usually is that the author thinks his writing is as highly specific and free from foggy notions and verbosity as he can make it. Criticism should be as crystal clear as the critic can make it, and as specific.

Authors should make every effort to determine who reads their reports. This audience should be carefully studied. The characteristics should be noted. Over-generalization should be avoided. No audience or readership is all-knowing, all-stupid, or stuffy, or eager. Supervisors? Subordinates? How much is known about the reader? Is this good?

In short, conduct a market survey. With a personal knowledge of the readers, and with an understanding of their interests and problems, authors can begin their report writing with the indispensable empathy.

CHAPTER 3

Ready, Aim, Fire!

Every engineer and scientist can *improve* his writing. All he needs to do is to continually seek to make each written piece better than the last. Remember what Epictetus said, "If you wish to be a writer, write." And as a well-known engineering editor remarked, "Other things being equal, skill with words will add between $20,000 and $100,000 to an engineer's lifetime earnings." Today many firms pay their engineers and scientists an honorarium for the preparation of worthy articles or papers. Narda Microwave Corporation awards a bonus to its engineers for a superior technical paper *before* it has been accepted for publication. So the rewards for good writing are well worth the effort.

Authors have spent hours waiting for inspiration, the right moment, the right mood, or the right word to start writing.

Never wait.

These excuses are nothing but self-justification for the lack of author preparedness. With an idea to be communicated and a strong knowledge of who should receive the message, the author should first gather and organize his facts and information.

The writer may do a literature search, or conduct interviews, experiments, or a survey to gather facts supporting his opinions.

Note Taking

Most research workers take their literature notes on 3 x 5 or 4 x 6 file cards. The three essential parts of the contents of a note card are:

(1) The material—the facts and opinions—to be recorded.

(2) The exact source, title and page number, from which they are taken.

(3) A label for the card, showing what it treats. This label is often called a *subject heading*.

Punched cards are ideally suited for larger bibliographies of the sort where the information may be used or referred to many times during the writing of a report. A punched card is a card on which alphabetical or numerical information may be represented by means of punched holes or slots. There are two types of punched cards available: edge-notched (Keysort) cards in which the information is represented by slots punched around the margin of the card, and the machine-tabulated card (IBM and Remington Rand) in which the information is punched in the form of rectangular or round holes on the face of the card. Since the face of the edge-notched card is not used for coding, it is possible to write or type on it a longer summary or abstract. Also with this sort of card the file may be kept at the author's desk and the information needed found in a few seconds with a sorting spindle.*

Coordinate indexing, a ponderous term for a simple scheme, is an alternative system of keeping notes in a convenient manner. All references and notecards are assigned a serial number. A card of convenient size is used and an arbitrarily chosen term or set of terms may be used for a heading. An old scheme, it has been systematized and championed as the *Uniterm System,* introduced about 1953. Much can be said in favor of the Uniterm System for personal index files. See Figure 1 for keyword cards showing accession numbers of indexed reports.

The units of information in the system are called *keywords*— terms that describe the subject matter embodied in a report. Although keywords generally are single words, they may even be proper names, trade names, or numbers. Typical keywords are *polypropylene, p-xylene, Tenite butyrate,* and *critical shear rate.*

Each keyword is typed as a heading on a separate card, which

* A good reference on the use of punched cards is: Casey, R. S., Perry, J. W., Kent, A., and Berry, M. M., "Punched Cards: Their Application to Science and Industry," 2nd ed., Reinhold Pub. Corp., New York, 1958.

is placed in alphabetical order in the card file. An accession (serial) number is assigned to each report as it is received. After the report has been indexed, the accession number is posted on the card for each keyword which pertains to that report. The keyword card *extrusion,* for example, contains the accession numbers of all reports pertaining to extrusion.

Keywords are considered *concepts,* and information is retrieved by *concept coordination.* Suppose, for example, the author wishes to retrieve all reports pertaining to the extrusion of polyamide films. The keywords are *extrusion, polyamides,* and *films.* In the keyword file there would be a card for each of the three concepts. Figure 1 shows the keyword cards *extrusion, polyamides,* and *films*

Extrusion

0	1	2	3	4	5	6	7	8	9
90	41	22	33	104	75	46	77	98	109
270	101	592		1194	115	716	157	478	219
	291	2502				986	307	888	839
						1136	1317		1009

Polyamides

0	1	2	3	4	5	6	7	8	9
90	31	52	1123	104	125	56	57	148	209
370	131	1002		794	225	286	497	328	789
1300	291	1852		1394	525	816	1197	438	
		2502		2564	1015			888	

Films

0	1	2	3	4	5	6	7	8	9
120	21	702	1123	104	15	76	17	88	109
890	141	1492		514	145	186		178	309
	291	1952		784	305	326		528	809
	401	2502		1004	1055	786		888	

FIGURE. 1. Keyword cards showing accession numbers of indexed reports.

with the accession numbers of reports pertaining to each keyword posted on that keyword card. The numeral at the top of each column represents the last digit of the accession numbers posted in that column.

Accession number 90 appears on both the *extrusion* and the *polyamides* keyword cards; therefore, the report represented by accession number 90 contains information on "extrusion of polyamides" but not on "extrusion of polyamide films." The reports represented by accession numbers 1123 and 109 contain information on "polyamide films" and "extrusion of films," respectively. Accession numbers 291, 2502, 104, and 888 appear on all three keyword cards; therefore, the four reports represented by these accession numbers contain information on "extrusion of polyamide films." The search may be made more specific by coordination with more keywords, such as *nylon 6,* to specify the polyamide.

In the future, searches may be made by means more advanced than visual comparison of accession numbers on keyword cards, but the principle—concept coordination—will not change.

The effectiveness of the system in yielding information from a search depends entirely on use of the proper keywords for putting information into the system. In other words, the output can be no better than the input. An author should therefore select carefully the keywords for indexing his report.

Notes need not be taken in full sentences; words, phrases, or topics are enough. Rules for what the author should take in his notes cannot be laid down. His judgment will tell him what is best, but here are two general points that apply to all topics:

(1) Distinguish between the author's claims of facts and opinions. Label and give credit later to the opinions.

(2) Distinguish carefully between direct quotation and summary of the writer's material; take as little quotation as possible, carefully marking with quotation marks.

Notebooks

Laboratory notebooks are a common medium for note taking among experimental scientists. Poor note taking in lab notebooks can result in a poor report simply because the author cannot remember why or what he had done and his records did not refresh his memory sufficiently.

A common fault is self-delusion. The experimenter is so impressed by what he finds at the moment that he honestly believes he will never forget. Furthermore, what he has found has suggested interesting further work and he can't take the time to write in his notebook. Every lab man has been guilty of this fault at some time in his life. It is the disciplined adult that keeps a neat, complete notebook.

Another common fault that results in poor note taking is poor planning. Most laboratory work today is part of a team effort with several, if not many, people working on the same project. Lab notebooks should be kept in such a manner that work done elsewhere can be logically incorporated into the notes, either by leaving appropriately labeled and dated space for results to be inserted or by instituting a well-indexed cross-reference system.

A third common fault in keeping lab notebooks consists of neglecting to record the thinking, although meticuously recording the doing. Many times the report writer faced with a mass of data cannot recall why he took some of it. The purpose of an experiment should always be recorded, no matter how simple or how obvious.

Scribbling notes on the backs of old envelopes or old management memos is obviously hazardous, but this practice will continue in spite of everything that has been said against it. Whenever this is done, however, the notes ought to be transferred as soon as possible to the lab notebook, signed and dated for legal reasons, and explained and expanded for technical reasons, explaining why and how in more detail.

The growing practice of taking data in the form of automatically recorded charts poses record-keeping problems. These charts represent original data and should be accorded the same treatment as data that is normally entered in the lab notebook. Few things are as frustrating as an unlabeled IR curve. The directly pertinent information, date, sample details, etc., should be written directly on the chart paper and cross-referenced to the experimental plan or purpose in the lab notebook. This cross referencing can often be accomplished by merely placing the notebook page number on the chart paper. A large collection of automatically recorded charts often creates storage problems and the dog-eared sheets tend to become unmanageable. Flat, unfolded storage is always best.

Some laboratories are incorporating modern data-processing techniques in their research lab note-taking operations. In these cases rigid adherence to prescribed principles of complete information stored in the permanent lab notebook legibly must be meticulously observed. Laboratories where this technique has been followed for some years have been rewarded in many respects.

Analysis

When the author is analyzing the assembled data, he should consider carefully the purpose and scope of his writing. Will his report inform, give advice, suggest change, or motivate readers? The answer to these questions will have great influence on the degree of detail and the placement of emphasis in the report.

The reader will not have had the author's advantage of close contact with the problem. The author's job is to tell convincingly and logically what the problem was, how it was attacked, and what the results were. He must be as objective as possible and not assume that the reader will have a deep interest in minor side issues which happened to fascinate the author. For example, the author may be enthusiastic about the statistical analysis he made regarding the reproducibility of his data. However, most readers will be quite satisfied with the simple statement that a standard statistical analysis procedure was used and that it showed a precision of thus and so. Similarly, while the author may be pleased with his excellent detective work which led to the discovery that certain of the early runs were in error due to a change in the calibration of a meter, it suffices to say that the results prior to Test 14 were corrected after a recalibration of the flowmeter.

Since the assembled material is of varying reliability and importance for the purposes of the report or paper, it should be gone over, sorted, and evaluated. This is the stage for questions. Is this statement accurate? Is this book reliable—in its facts, in its reasoning? Is there enough material for the paper proposed? Have all the best sources been tried? Should more experiments be run or should some be rerun? Can more material be gathered by talking to someone? Have the most important phases been covered? Which are the most important facts and conclusions for the paper? Which are of secondary importance? Can all reasonable questions of the reader be answered?

Definitive Statement

It will help to achieve a coherent, forthright paper if the author composes a specific statement—not a title, but a sentence—of the subject as he sees it after the material has been gathered and thought about. A sentence statement of the purpose of a particular paper might be: "The hobby of building miniature aircraft is instructive and in wartime has become genuinely useful." That statement would define the author's approach—not personal, though his experiences would be his source of details, but topical. It suggests that he might touch briefly on the hobby phase to gain interest and make contact with his reader, and then select facts about different models, identifying some types, perhaps with diagrams, and stressing especially the wartime use of the models. Such a topical statement will let the author examine his miscellaneous material in the light of a definite purpose, help him decide to discard some and highlight other points; it serves as a touchstone for deciding whether a certain bit of material belongs in the paper or not.

In making this survey of material, it is helpful to sort out essential points that must be included and contributing points that may or may not be used, perhaps for illustration, depending on circumstances which may develop later in the actual writing.

The result of this stage should be a sifted body of material with which the author is thoroughly familiar, brought in line with the purpose of the report, and selected after considering its interest, accuracy, and importance for his purpose.

Outline

No good report can be written without some sort of outline. A very experienced writer can sometimes do a well-organized report without a *written* outline, but even then he has a clear mental outline. Writers tend to skip making an outline because they regard it as a chore, not realizing that they are losing a tremendous aid in organizing their report. Most writers recall the mechanics of outline preparation with its parallel construction, its numeral-letter-numeral-letter classification sequence, absence of punctuation, and poetic style of capitalization. With more thought on content and less on form, outline preparation can cease to be a chore and can become, in fact, the medium for the utmost in the thrill of writing. The author has the opportunity, while preparing an outline, to compose as fast as his mind will travel through the logical patterns he wishes his reader to perceive. The emphasis among "desk men" on secretaries and tape recorders emphasizes the mechanical problem many of us have in recording our thinking word for word fast enough to keep up with the flashing logic of our mental processes. For the lab man the outline usually solves the problem. With an orderly outline in hand, it is much easier to return leisurely to turning phrases well and seeking precise wording without the nagging fear of losing the point. Technical writing requires the discipline of an outline.

Layout for Tables and Charts

In a simple report it should be possible to prepare substantially finished tables and figures without fear of undue revision. However, for a more complicated report, a helpful method is to rough out a set of dummy tables and charts indicating only the general content, coordinates, significant data, etc. This permits subsequent revision, if it appears advisable, without losing the time spent on carefully prepared tables or graphs. Moreover, quickly preparing rough layouts tends to give the writer perspective, and insures uniformity of the several figures and tables.

Besides a good stock of material, the feeling of being ready to write is the best guarantee of a good paper. This is the prime result of careful work in the early steps.

Rough Draft

The first draft should be written rapidly without consideration for grammar, punctuation, or spelling.

The author shouldn't spend much time searching for an ideal opening—this can become a sort of procrastination. The report must be started some way if it is to be written at all, so it is wise to make a tentative start, the best that suggests itself at the moment, and change it later. After a few pages the writing will be better, and many times a good opening will be found by simply crossing out the first paragraph or two. If the material has been well laid out, it is relatively easy to concentrate on one stage at a time and not lose energy by trying to think of everything at once.

This doesn't mean that the first draft should be careless, but simply that it is a means and not an end. For most people, the first draft should be a rather rapid writing of the material. The report will have more life and will represent the author's sense of his material more closely if it is written rapidly than if he pauses to perfect each sentence before going on to the next. It is usually fatal to stop to look up spelling or to check mechanics at the time of writing. Save time for revising so that the business of tending to such small but important matters can be handled. In a first draft leave plenty of space between lines, between paragraphs, and in margins to allow for editing. It is probably better to make the first draft a fully detailed description of the material, because it is always easier to take out unwanted matter than to expand topics that have been done too briefly.

When the first draft is completed and the writer has exhausted his material, the manuscript should be put away to *cool* as long as the author's schedule will allow. Several weeks is best, but a day is essential. Absence makes the report grow objective! When the manuscript is brought out again, the all-important editing may begin.

Revision

The initial step in checking the first draft is to read it quickly to see that all points are covered, and that the text develops the subject tersely but without ambiguity to the concluding thoughts.

Assign in sequence final figure and table numbers and prepare finished copies of each. Sometimes the preparation of these tables and figures brings out unforeseen items requiring comment in the text. The author should remember that the impression left by a well-written report can be spoiled by ill-drawn graphs and poor illustrations.

In general, data should be presented in either figures or tables, but not duplicated in these or in the text. Use of several figures which present the same data from slightly different angles should be avoided.

The proper arrangement of a table may be difficult. If a table is complicated, the author should consult an editor, or colleague, or typist for help in establishing its proper form. The best advice in print to my knowledge may be found in a paper by E. Cortelyou, "Some Fundamentals of Designing Tables of Data," *J. Chem. Educ.* **31,** 590 (1954). This reprint has since been revised but the principles of table layout remain unchanged.

In preparing a tabulation the following general rules will help the reader follow the presentation. The sequence of data columns should be so chosen that the change of the principal variable from left to right is progressive in logic rather than in the chronological order of taking the data. Graphs are preferable to tables for most readers. Where the significant data are given in an appended table or chart, it is a convenience to the reader to have the principal trend given in the text.

For example: "Chart 2 shows that the curve of octane number plotted against reactor temperature reaches a maximum of 96 octane number at 50°F, falling off rapidly to 89 octane number at 0°F and 100°F."

Charts and tables should clearly state the source, applicability, and scope of the data in the titles and notes, in case they become separated from the report.

The author should remember that tables are to be typed or set in type by people who are not chemists, physicists, or engineers, and that the prime requisite of a manuscript table is legibility. The typists or printers should not be compelled to guess at the matter in the table or at the way in which it should be arranged. The writing should not be crowded. Paper is cheaper than the time of anyone who has to handle the table after it is first compiled.

In reviewing the manuscript the author may look at his work much as if it were a piece of architecture. It must not only perform the function for which it is designed in a logical and orderly manner, but it should appeal to the esthetic sense. The architect synthesizes the utilitarian needs of the building into a pleasing structure, considering the design of the facade, the color and texture of the building materials used, the decorations of the cornice, and many other things. With something of the same approach the report writer should go about refining his manuscript. He should give careful consideration to the choice of words—for words have color and texture—to the arrangement of these words into sentences, and to the proper division of the text into paragraphs. In the end his report will be more likely to stimulate the reader's intellect.

Clarity and Conciseness

Clarity requires that the writer's thoughts be presented directly and without ambiguity. The efficiency and beauty of a simple declarative sentence can be considered as the medium for scientific communication. Please, use it. Avoid the complicated, meandering sentence in which the meaning is muddled by complex construction.

Completeness is as significant to a report as clarity. A thought should be conveyed completely enough for the meaning to be perfectly clear. No reader can be assumed to possess all the background information that an author has on the subject matter of his paper.

Therefore, it takes extra care to present a complete and continuous story and one that has no serious discontinuities and illogical sequences for the reader. However, the author should not include information the reader does not need to understand the message.

Coleridge wrote, "The art of writing consists largely in knowing what to leave in the inkwell."

Conciseness requires that the author's thought be expressed without irrelevancies and superfluous words. Avoid vague and inexact words. Be quantitative, as much so as the subject permits. Avoid idle words. Make every word useful. Clarity and completeness require more words, and conciseness requires fewer; so the author is tugged in two directions. But his goal is to achieve a balance between these opposing forces. Brevity is a virtue in technical writing, but it can be over-used. The shortest paragraph is not necessarily the clearest, and a crystal clear, closely knit sentence is valueless if it does not present adequate information. A style that is too abrupt and terse creates a sense of urgency and leaves the reader gasping.

"It is best to be brief and complete, but it is better to be wordy than misunderstood," said J. H. Wilson in "A Few Hints on Word Usage," *J. Chem. Ed.*, **33**, 577 (1956).

The writer owes brevity to the publishing journal, since costs are high and competition for space is keen. In technical reports, the reader's time is often so limited that he does not pay attention to full details of the work. The author of such reports should be as brief as is consistent with the intent of his report, but he ought to write summaries or abstracts for time-savers. A short, concise discussion accompanied by complete detail is a good combination.

Economy and accuracy mean using the straightforward English sentence with all parts showing: subject, verb, and object. Follow a consistent pattern of tense. Use the present tense for generalizations and references to stable conditions, and record observations, data, and experiments in the past tense.

Illustrations are valuable aids to clarity and conciseness. Graphs, tables, drawings, photographs, etc. convey the writer's thought by presenting large amounts of concentrated information clearly and fully.

Directness and Continuity

Directness in writing means that the main thought is presented with the most emphasis.

If the temperature is changed, if the pH is changed, or if agitation is stopped, the enzymic reaction is ended.

In this short sentence the main idea is: Enzymic reaction ends if conditions change. So a more direct way of writing this type of sentence would be:

Enzymic reaction ends if the temperature, pH, or agitation is changed.

Inverted sentences have their place where the conditions need emphasis, but normal word order usually expresses the point with the proper emphasis and least misunderstanding for the reader.

It is good to let the manuscript "cool" again before beginning the final polishing. Many errors in spelling, grammar, change in style, or faulty expressions can be seen easily when the author has been away from his writing for a few days.

Sections and paragraphs should be checked to ensure that continuity exists—that the main thought flows smoothly through the report. The writer ought to see that the reader's thoughts at the end of each paragraph are prepared for the next. He should make sure that the first sentence of each paragraph and section introduces the subject. Never depend on the section title as a topic sentence. Most readers do not absorb the significance of a subtitle, and the thought should be repeated in the first sentence.

Sentences should carry only one basic thought, but care should be used to avoid a series of jerky, staccato sentences. The use of compound sentences and sentences containing dependent clauses will do much to improve the readability of a number of bald, simple sentences. Too much repetition of the subject can be avoided by intelligent use of pronouns. Usually it is better to place a dependent clause at the end of a sentence if the clause is a transition to the subsequent sentences, and vice versa.

Length of a paragraph is governed by the complexity of the subject matter and the qualifications of the reader. A paragraph ought to be long enough to present its subject adequately and not so long as to make reading burdensome. There is nothing as forbidding as an unbroken expanse of black type—a solid pageful of words. The most effective arrangement is short paragraphs mixed with fewer long ones.

Grammar, spelling, and punctuation should be carefully checked during the final polishing.

Simple Writing

Technical reports should be written as simply as is consistent with the topic. "Fine writing" and uncommon or "high sounding" words or phrases are out of place in reports and should be omitted. Correct terminology should be used, but being too technical to be understood by those who are not specialists in the particular subject is often an obnoxious form of bragging.

Common practice dictates that reports should be impersonal. Much has been said during the past decade on the use of personal references and personal pronouns in technical report writing. In spite of strong advice from writing experts, there is little evidence that scientific journals approve of the use of "I" in writing technical papers.

In less formal reports where circulation may not be so widespread and editing may not be governed so closely by conservative forces, the use of "I" and "my," "our" and "we" will do a great deal to make the writing more readable. The use of the personal pronouns makes the use of active verbs much more logical and easy for authors. Active verbs used with the subject "the author" in place of a personal pronoun fails on all counts, and should be avoided.

Vivid and graphic writing results from the use of words and expressions which impart exact meanings. Critical study of each word and each phrase will do much to restrict the meaning and to eliminate ambiguities. Avoid using the words "small," "large," "few," "many," "several," and "not often." Substitute definite for approximate quantities. Early in the report give the reader the benefit of more definite identification of the unit discussed than merely a code nmber. For example, *XRD-4* might mean little to most readers whereas *the X-ray diffraction unit, XRD-4* identifies it immediately. The same can be said for *A-20* and *Mark IV*.

The following words and expressions illustrate the type of improvement that can be made by careful revision of expression:

Poor	Good
Entirely satisfactory	Satisfactory
Proportioned out	Proportioned
Completely full	Full
Check up	Check
Drop down	Drop
Great variety	Variety
Very accurately	Accurately
The amount of time saved	The time saved
The interval should have a length of four seconds	The interval of time should be four seconds
At the present time	Now, or at present (not "presently")
An attempt was made to show an estimate of the value of	An attempt was made to estimate the value of
In respect to depreciation, it will be testified to by the next witness	The next witness will testify on depreciation
Due to the heat, the work could not continue	Because of the heat the work could not continue
In the case of failure of the lines	If the lines fail
In connection with the ordering of parts	When ordering parts

During this final checking the needs of the readers, determined at the beginning of the writing effort, should be referred to. If the readers' needs seem to be met to the best of the author's ability, he might well set down the names of these readers as a distribution list to prepare the manuscript for publication.

Dissemination

Each organization, of course, tailors its distribution practices to its own needs. Many follow a three-step program:

(1) Limited initial distribution.

(2) Wide dissemination of abstracts.

(3) Ready availability of copies for reference purposes when "desire to know" has been indicated.

Here again the primary scientific journals display a conservative attitude. Under pressure of the need for more rapid dissemination of research and development reports, some of the technical societies have instituted "express journals" to provide an opportunity for authors to record an early date for their discoveries in fields of rapid change, such as physics. In time, perhaps, the technical journals will follow the lead of the less formal reporting organizations, such as government contractors.

The abstracts serve to call new subject matter to the attention of a broader group than that covered by the "need to know" criterion. Those who "desire to know" have only to signify, and the reports can be made available to them.

It is usually at this point that a security determination is made, whether the report is written under government or industrial auspices. Research reports often represent tremendous past expenditures, but their potential can affect the balance sheet of any company or provide for the defense of the nation. Freedom of scientific expression must be tempered with judgment!

Responsibility is the price of freedom.

Final Polishing

After the report is substantially complete, a last check should be made to see that all data are accurately recorded and are consistent between text and tables or charts. Also the correct reference numbers for tables, figures, and charts must be checked in the text, and the bibliography page numbers, volume, and year need to be verified.

Neatness of the manuscript is important. Illegibility, excessive inserts, erasures, and cancelled lines, although not a road-block to having a well-written report once it has been typed, certainly make for a poor reception of the manuscript when submitted for approval. Moreover, a sloppy draft taxes the ingenuity of the typist or editor to decipher it correctly.

At this stage it is helpful to have someone who can understand the report read it critically. Co-workers, editors, and librarians are frequently called upon in industry to give candid reactions to polished report manuscripts. The author should pay attention to their comments. Their reaction is probably very close to that of the author's intended readership.

The final typing of a report must be done with diligence and not merely in a perfunctory manner. Typographical errors are not only embarrassing, but may actually mislead the reader.

"A professor of chemistry at *X* University has received a $4,500 grant from the *Y* Research Fund for a study of the instability constants of complexions."

Since the professor and the school as well as the Fund, all obviously have a sincere interest in complex ions, they will not be embarrassed again by identification. This quote was taken from one of the leading newspapers in the country, the *St. Louis Post Dispatch*. It illustrates the importance of the most minute error— a missing space. Many readers may believe that this professor is studying cosmetics and their effects on skin.

Every report should, if possible, be checked by a person other than the original writer. In order to do this properly, the proofreader should read the report "once over lightly," merely making mental notes of what he believes might be improved. A scrutinizing reading should then be undertaken in which mathematical figures are checked, the choice of words and syntax are subjected to critical appraisal, and the conclusions and recommendations of the report are examined for soundness of reasoning.

If there are many corrections or if they are complicated, the page should be done over. If they are relatively small, like inserting a letter or a word, or substituting a single word, this can usually be done neatly without damaging the page. The goal is clean, legible copy that can be read by another. A carbon copy of the manuscript should be made and retained by the author, and the original (not the carbon) should be transmitted for publication.

Production

To the printer, "copy" is manuscript or matter to be set in type. The first type proof is called a "galley proof" because the type is assembled in brass trays called galleys. The first galley proof is checked against the original copy by the printer's proofreader and then by the author; it is then corrected, and a second proof is taken. After it has been revised (that is, compared with the corrected first galley), it is converted into pages and printed as the finished report. Galley proof will ordinarily be sent to the author; also page proof if desirable and practicable. If the report needs an index, that is made from the page proof.

The proofs will bear marks made by the proofreader and editors—corrections, suggestions, and queries. Definition and usage examples of proofreaders' marks are presented clearly and adequately on page 1051 of *Webster's Seventh New Collegiate Dictionary*. Every good dictionary has a section on "preparation of copy for the press," with suggestions, printing terms and proofreaders' marks.

These marks on the proof should be carefully noted, and special attention should be given to queries—question marks on the margins of proof sheets opposite points at which doubt is indicated, inconsistencies are noted, information is wanted, or blanks are to be filled. Failure to note and answer such queries may necessitate the return of the proofs to the author again, with delay in the final printing.

Only reasonable corrections can be made in the galley proof, not radical alterations; and only slight, inexpensive changes will be permitted in the pages. As a rule additions can be made only on the galleys. In making changes the author should keep in mind that the alteration of a few words at the opening of a paragraph may require the resetting of the whole paragraph, and in linotype work the alteration of a single comma requires the resetting of a whole line.

If a considerable amount of matter is to be added, it should be written on a sheet or slip, which should be pinned or clipped (not pasted) to the galley proof, and the place at which the added matter is to be inserted should be clearly indicated. Proof should be corrected and returned promptly with the original manuscript unchanged to the editor.

A report may be mimeographed or duplicated by direct image offset (commonly called Multilith) instead of set in type.

These two methods of reproduction are in widespread use for up to several thousand copies. In combination with the diazo process (Ozalid), these systems provide much cheaper duplication facilities, since the copy is prepared on the typewriter, requires no galleys for proofreading, allows erasure for correction, and produces copy of a quality distinguishable from typesetting only by the most practiced eye.

When the final copy comes in, it should be assembled and bound neatly and then sent out according to the proper distribution list.

A plastic spiral spine for binding allows the reader the convenience of leaving the report open flat during interruptions of his reading and avoids the irritation of having copy bound so close to the stitching as to make reading difficult. Every thought from note taking to binding should be with the reader in mind.

CHAPTER 4 *Divisions of a Report*

The Bureau of Naval Weapons launched a project KISS in 1960. The project was aimed at improving communication. The letters stood for "Keep it simple, stupid."

Reports are written in sections to make the reading simple. Division headings are only labels to permit the reader to select portions of interest. The many possible divisions are discussed here to help authors organize their material systematically. Putting conclusions in footnotes or references (often done) misleads the reader and severely damages the effectiveness of the message.

Reports differ from one another in so many ways that one cannot categorically list the divisions that must be used in writing all reports. Discussed below are many of the divisions which may occur in a report. Few reports, however, can be divided as extensively as described here. These divisions, while falling in a logical sequence, are, furthermore, not necessarily listed in the order in which they should always appear in a report.

A title and introduction should precede the body of any report. A topical report (contrasted with some progress reports) often contains an abstract or summary as well. It is hoped that each author who reads this chapter will follow the directions for an abstract given here. Incorrectly written abstracts are misleading, frustrating, and even worse, frequently useless.

Title

The title should appear on the first manuscript page and should be as short as is consistent with clarity. It should suggest the contents of the report as specifically as possible. However, it is necessary to exercise considerable care to be certain that the subject selected is the one by which the report will most logically be remembered at a later date. Titles should not convey too little, or suggest more than is contained in the substance of the work.

Far more attention and significance is attached to titles by readers than is given by most authors. The rapid rise in the volume of literature that must be skimmed to find what should be read has developed a broad practice of glancing at titles (sometimes summaries) to determine whether or not to read on. Readers use titles as a rough screen of what to read. Newspapers, recognizing this reader habit, have long used the headline to "hook" readers.

Remember the indexer. He is among the readers and is influential in securing future readers. A writer should not go so far in trying to be interesting that he gets cute with his title. This practice leaves a sour taste in the mouth of the reader who is misled; it is especially dangerous for indexers.

"A Two-Edged Sword" might be a fine title for a speech (particularly a sermon), but it is poor as a technical writing title. What subject is it referring to? There are "two-edged swords" in every area of life. A title like this, even though it actually referred to a problem of control of aquatic herbicides would probably be filed under "Sword" or "Armaments" in some indexes.*

Technical writers must give increasing attention to the wording of titles. Pressure to improve titles comes from two recent developments in documentation.

In the past few years an increasing number of organizations have copied report titles and tables of contents of journals into bulletins that they distributed to their clientele to assist in determining what to read. Report announcement bulletins and tables-of-contents services may often be the only "hook" available to an author to reach important readers.

Chemical Abstracts Service was the first to issue a regular publication using this new technique with titles. From their experience

* Stevens, J. D., "Writing Better Titles and Abstracts," Tech. Extension Service, Wash. State Univ., Pullman, Wash., 1961 (Wash. State Inst. Tech. Bull.).

with unedited titles R. B. Freeman, of the *Chemical Abstracts Service,* had the following to say about what a title should convey for a paper describing some aspect of chemistry.

"The method of writing a title should be changed from a haphazard process to some systematic one such as one consisting of (1) writing down the key words which express the aspects of the paper and (2) joining these key words through the use of connectives. For a chemical paper the aspects involve specific substances (fluorothene), properties (phase equilibria), transformations (Friedel-Crafts Reaction), and their relationships to the environment (in organic solvents). Not all aspects will be relevant in every title, of course."

The following are four titles which might be used for the same paper:

(1) Solubility Studies

(2) Solubility of Fluorothene

(3) Phase Equilibria Between Fluorothene and Organic Solvents

(4) A Study of the Phase Equilibria between Fluorothene and Some Solvents such as Dibutyl Phthalate and Chlorotrifluoroethylene at Elevated Temperatures

In these examples title (3) is the best compromise between brevity and information. There are a few other generalizations that may assist in title writing.

(1) Avoid verbs. Titles are not sentences or headlines.

(2) Avoid articles; "the," "an," "a," etc. are useless here where brevity is of first importance.

(3) Avoid clauses. Clauses require introductory words that lengthen titles unduly.

(4) Avoid numbers and complex symbolism. Technical titles should be informative, not mysterious.

(5) Short means less than 80 characters including spaces. Computers print 10 characters to the inch and the programs producing "permuted indexes" allow only one line per title.

(6) "Informative" means terms that readers know. Introduce new terms later in the report.

Only the first letter of each principal word should be capitalized and such superfluous words as "Study of," "Investigation of," "A

Final Report on," or "A Complete Investigation of" should not appear.

Authors can control the quality of indexing for their reports by beginning immediately to write brief but informative titles themselves.

The headings of subdivisions also should be brief and descriptive of the material following them. A heading at any level should be followed by at least a phrase of introductory discussion or explanation before material under a subheading within that division is introduced.

The first sentence in each division or subdivision of a report should be complete within itself; that is, it should never depend upon the heading of that division for its full meaning, even though repetition of several words from the heading may be necessary. Headings guide the reader in finding specific sections and indicating complete topics. The serious reader often reads over headings without seeing them. They should be used as guideposts, not part of the highway of thought.

Authors

The choice and order of listing of authors of a technical report is frequently a source of misunderstanding. These misunderstandings can usually be avoided if there is a clear agreement at the time the work is started. The following principles should apply:

(1) The authors of a technical report should be those who have actually carried out the experimental work and who have written the report.

(2) The senior author, who historically is listed first, should be the person who has made the largest contribution to the solution of the problem, not the one who has done the most writing for the report.

(3) The contribution of major ideas should be acknowledged along with other significant help in the acknowledgments.

The matter of authorship of a paper which an editor has written, yet which contains the data and conclusions of others, is a policy which must be established clearly among those concerned. In all cases, of course, the man whose work is being reported must be the senior author. It is usually more satisfactory if the editorial writer receives no publicity, or perhaps a note of acknowledgment instead of joint authorship, unless, of course, he is also an authority in the field involved and has contributed something to the paper other than its clear and adequate statement.

There are occasions in all organizations when administrative progress reports, or commentary articles on external developments from a company viewpoint must be prepared; yet it is important to morale as well as ethics that they bear specific authorship. Fortunately, many men in responsible positions in the scientific field possess the ability to write, but even then they do not always have sufficient time to allot to such endeavors and must delegate the actual work to others, just as they delegate the performance of given production tasks or research projects. The man who actually writes the article (ghost writer) must do it from the viewpoint of the individual under whose by-line it will appear; he must state such facts, arguments, and conclusions as the "author" would do if he prepared it for himself; and he must in every way be the "mouthpiece" of the man for whom he is writing. A certain amount of such administrative ghost writing is necessary and reasonably ethical, and it often falls to the lot of the technical editors in those organizations which employ them. However, when it comes to ghost writing for those who ought to be able to prepare their own papers and should take time for this important job, the ethics are more than dubious.

There is some question of the ethics of complete rewriting by an editor. The writing of papers using data supplied by another for publication under the writer's name is even more questionable, and the individual supplying the data learns little by this effort about his own data and conclusions to be drawn from it. He is therefore no better able to prepare his next paper. Recourse to such measures should be undertaken only in emergencies, and their continuation should definitely be discouraged.

Writing is the description of one's thoughts, and a scientist who cannot communicate his thoughts loses a large measure of his value. It is, therefore, a grave reflection on any technical man to be unable to write both willingly and fluently. Ghost writing can be done at least two ways. The scientist can explain his experiments, discuss the literature, review the results, and tell the ghost writer his conclusions, or the scientist may permit the ghost writer to perform these mental functions for him. In the latter case the scientists has reduced himself to a laboratory technician. Ultimately, through lack of practice, he will be unable to draw logical conclusions, discuss data, and critically review the literature. No scientist should permit this to happen. If he prefers to describe the entire report to the ghost writer, it would be cheaper, more efficient, and profoundly more useful to purchase a dictating machine.

Preface

Only in rare cases is it advisable to write a preface to a report. Such a preface should give information on the circumstances in existence prior to work on the project, but no detailed information about the work itself. The preface may well include acknowledgments of assistance, particularly that received from other laboraties. It may include the author's explanation of why the report was written, something of the author's background, experience, or thinking that led to the writing of the report, how he hopes the report will be used, or some significant details of history. It is frequently written by someone other than the report author, such as a noted authority or the author's sponsor. It should not be confused with the introduction.

Table of Contents

The table of contents is a topical outline of the report, together with page numbers. The entries in the table of contents are the exact headings which appear throughout the body of the report to mark the various divisions of the text. The table of contents has several functions. From it the reader can learn what subjects are treated in the report, the relative value given related topics, and the order in which they are developed. The table of contents is also a reference device by which the parts of the report may be

located by page number. In this latter function, a detailed table of
contents is particularly desirable in a long report which does not
have an index.

References, appendix, and index should be listed in the table of
contents in the same type style as division headings.

Lists of tables, figures, and illustrations sometimes appear in reports much the same as a table of contents. This is an archaic policy
and should be ignored. This Victorian practice of listing tables,
figures, and illustrations may increase the apparent length of the
report; it may impress the ignorant; it may even be used to sub-
vert the reader's thinking that this kind of listing is in good form.
But authors interested in better report writing will let the practice
die. It lends nothing to the report but length and pomposity.

Abstract

A long paper should be accompanied by an abstract, preferably
at the beginning. This abstract is not part of the paper, but an
adjunct intended to convey briefly the content of the paper, in the
manner of a preview. It draws attention to all new information and
to the main conclusions. It helps prospective readers decide whether
to read the entire report.

An abstract provides "current awareness" for the researcher;
that is, it provides an aid in keeping up with what is going on. It
is a definite research tool used by the reader for actual technical
information or references to its source. This "reference function"
concerns an abstract's usefulness one, two, five, ten, or more years
after publication, when it may serve in the preparation of bibliographies or reviews of the literature in a special field.

Abstracts are usually thought of as falling into two general types.
An *indicative* (or descriptive) abstract is short, and is written solely
to enable the reader to decide whether he should read the original
article. This type of abstract also enables the reader to follow the
report more intelligently—he knows what to expect in the paper.

An *informative* abstract summarizes the article's major arguments and gives the principal data and conclusions which the abstractor considers make a valuable contribution to knowledge or

are likely to be of use to the specific class of readers for whom the abstract is prepared, such as the busy reader who is interested in the material but cannot read the entire report and must rely on the abstract. Numerical results are entirely appropriate in this abstract. It should contain specific information and avoid the vague or the general. For example, if the search for an effective respiratory stimulant is the major problem in the report, the general statement

A potent respiratory stimulant acting through the central respiratory centers was found.

is less valuable than

Doxapram hydrochloride, 1-ethyl-4-(2-morpholinoethyl)-3,3-diphenyl-2-pyrrolidinone hydrochloride hydrate, has been shown to be a potent respiratory stimulant acting mainly through direct stimulation of central respiratory centers.

The separation between indicative and informative abstracts is not sharp, and technical abstracts as a whole, instead of falling tidily into two well-defined categories, actually form a kind of continuous spectrum of varying informativeness.

Also, by interpreting the term "abstract" a little more broadly, one can include the idea of critical review which gives the reader, in addition to information about what the article contains, the abstractor's opinion of its importance and technical stature. A few of the existing abstracting services, such as *Computer Abstracts*, published by ACM (Assoc. Computer Machinery), include this feature, usually combined with the informative type of abstract.

Many scientists prefer the indicative rather than the informative abstract because seldom, if ever, would they accept technical data and conclusions given in an abstract without themselves checking the original article. The ease with which original articles can be obtained varies greatly for different journals, and this favors the informativeness in abstracts of articles which are hard to come by.

For the author, the abstract is an opportunity to bring what he considers the important results of his work before his colleagues in condensed form. For his colleagues, it is a means of keeping in touch with a much larger field of scientific publication than they can otherwise cover. Also, by presenting a brief quotable summary of the report, it helps industrial management to disseminate knowledge of its work. An effective arrangement of an abstract is to include the following information directly and concisely:

(1) Why was the work done?
(2) What was done?
(3) What were the results?
(4) What do the results mean?

Although usually read first, the abstract should be written last. It should be written in normal rather than abbreviated English. Where possible, standard terms should be used and unnecessary contracting should be avoided. Third person is preferable. Mixed tenses, combining indicative and imperative forms, and examples amplifying the statement should be avoided.

Comparisons with the work of others or with what has been previously known about a topic should also be avoided. This does not exclude reference to the work of others if the present work is a development from theirs and it is necessary to show the basis upon which it is built.

Be as specific on each point as space allows. Don't state what the report is about, but what it tells. For example don't say, "Not all the primary minerals are detritral; some are formed in place." Say, "Not all the primary minerals are detrital; at least a part of the iron carbonate, titanate, and feldspars were formed in place."

An author should not say, "Azo dyes are prepared by the coupling of diazonium salts." He should say, "Azo dyes are prepared when a phenol or aryl amine is treated with a diazonium salt solution."

An author should not say, "The continuous process will reduce costs." He should say, "The continuous process requires 10% less raw material inventory and permits a 5% reduction in labor."

The author of an abstract can presume that the reader has some knowledge of the subject, but has not read the paper. The reader may not even have the paper available at all if he is working with the abstract journal or index cards. The abstract should, therefore, be intelligible in itself without reference to the paper. For example, it should not cite sections or illustrations as a substitute for a statement of their content. A series of sentences beginning, "This report

contains. . . ." or "This is a study of. . . ." or "An investigation of
. . . ." do not constitute an abstract.

Abstracts for *Chemical Abstracts Service* are designed specifically
for chemists. Their rules for writing abstracts govern the preparation of the most influential technical journal in the world. The
philosophy of their abstract writing is contained in these three
rules:

(1) The abstract should state newly observed facts, conclusions
of an experiment or argument, and, if possible, the essential parts
of any new theory, treatment, apparatus, technique, etc.

(2) It should contain the names of any new compound, and any
new numerical data, such as physical constants. If this is not possible, it should draw attention to them. It is important to refer to
new items and observations, even though they may be incidental
to the main purpose of the paper.

(3) When giving experimental results, the abstract should indicate the methods used. For new methods the basic principle,
range of operation, and degree of accuracy should be given.

A copy of *Directions for Abstractors* published by The Chemical
Abstracts Service of The American Chemical Society, October 1,
1964, can be obtained by writing to The Chemical Abstracts Service, Ohio State University, Columbus, Ohio 43210. In this small
book are examples for writing article abstracts, style and scope,
patent abstracts, abbreviations, nomenclature, and a set of proofreader's marks.

It is impossible to assign definite lengths to abstracts. In general,
short, compact papers require actually shorter but proportionately
longer abstracts than long, detailed papers. *The Journal of the
American Medical Society* requires not more than 200 words. *Revue
de géologie* sets low limits—not more than 125 words for a 5-page
article, 250 words for a 25-page article, and 1,200 words for the
longest reports. *Biological Abstracts* sets the upper limit at 3 percent of the length of the original paper. The abstracts in *Astrophysical Journal* and *Physical Review* and those from anthropologi-
cal articles average about 5 percent of the paper. Those in *Chemical
Abstracts* average considerably less, usually not exceeding 200
words. A reasonable maximum limit for an average paper of three

to five journal pages long would be 3 percent of the article wordage for the abstract.

The technical writer who has learned to abstract a five or six page patent or a ten to twelve page scientific report in four lines without omitting a basic idea has learned how to present his own ideas effectively.

Introduction

The introduction provides a convenient place for showing the reader the over-all plan of the report. It improves the readability of a long report or one involving generally unfamiliar material.

The reader must be oriented by this section so that the scheme of experimental procedure and discussion of the results may be clearly followed and understood. The introduction is *not* a rehash of the summary. Each introduction should be custom-built for a particular report. Few introductions will discuss all the following items, but this list is suggestive of the subject matter from which selections may be made:

(1) Subject, objectives, or purpose of the report.

(2) Current situation giving rise to the need of the study.

(3) The writer's understanding of the assignment.

(4) The writer's point of view or attitude toward the subject.

(5) Limitations, scope, or the extent of treatment and what the report is and is not.

(6) History, background, and review of previous reports in this subject.

(7) The basic theories, principles, or policies involved.

(8) Methods used to reach the conclusions.

(9) The sources of information.

(10) How the information was gathered.

(11) What information was used.

(12) The findings, briefly and incidentally stated.

(13) Concepts stated along with definitions of terms.

(14) The general plan followed in developing the solution.

(15) The plan and content of the report.

If the above items were developed in detail, the introduction would become a lengthy treatise—in fact, the report itself. Such development is not needed in the introduction, nor intended. Introductions to reports should be brief, concise, and helpful. The history, background, and definitions, when these items become too long for the introduction, may be placed in separate sections in the body of the report. The other items suggested may only be mentioned.

The minimum contents of an introduction should be:

(1) A statement of subject and objective.

(2) Clarification of the situation or circumstances which made the preparation of the report desirable.

(3) A brief explanation of the methods used.

Body

Following the introduction is the development of the body of the report. The body should contain the essential information for solving the problems described in the introduction and for arriving at sound conclusions and/or practical recommendations.

This is the detailed section of the report and usually consists of several parts, all of which are related, but the several parts may be distinct as to treatment. The subheadings for this part of the report depend entirely on the nature of the material and consequently are at the discretion of the author. In cases where the report is long enough, suitable divisions should be made to lead the reader through a logical sequence of thought. This is the experimental section and is the heart of technical writing. Details of procedure, measurement, equipment, and results are often found in the body under appropriate subheadings. This detailed information permits duplication of the experiments, critical evaluation of the work, and gives a detailed record of observations, measurements, constants, and new data.

Description of Materials. For the convenience of other experimental workers and those for whom the report is issued, the materials should be described in full so that they may be referred to readily on any occasion. For instance, equipment, chemicals, medicinals, etc., should be described in such a way that their origin and quality are clear. The names and addresses of suppliers of brand products should be provided. Details which might be considered significant if the work were to be repeated or tried by another worker ought to be included. Any unusual features should be discussed in the text. For example, if the sample is obtained under atypical operating conditions, the author should discuss any effects these conditions may have on plant streams other than the one under consideration.

It is inadequate to say, for example, "A sample of Plant 7-12 blowers constituted the charge stock." Better to write, "The charge consists of a sample of Plant 7-12 blowers obtained June 9, 1965, while this unit was operating in a normal manner for the production of charge stock used in the manufacture of air conditioners. The tests on the cooled air, which represent 40% relative humidity at 65°F, are given in Table III."

Experimental Procedure. This section is the core of technical writing. This concise description of methods and apparatus permits critical evaluation of the work, allows duplication of the experiments, and leaves a record of measurements, constants, and observations.

People directly concerned with the subject will read the experimental section. How much detail should be included in this section? It is better for the reader to plow through superfluous material to find the specific information he needs than not to find the information at all. And even though this excessive detail is the lesser of two evils, no one likes unnecessary words. As W. J. Gensler and K. D. Gensler succinctly advise in their fine book, *Writing Guide for Chemists,** "The writer must be selective; he does not have carte blanche to dump the contents of his laboratory notebook indiscriminately into the experimental section."

A certain amount of latitude is permissible in the presentation of this material, such as description of the apparatus, equipment, conditions used, and data obtained. Obviously, if the equipment or tests are not standard, nor previously identified, they should be adequately described here so that the work can be duplicated by

* McGraw-Hill Book Co., Inc., New York, 1961.

others and the accuracy and precision can be judged. If the apparatus or equipment used is complicated but has been described elsewhere in detail, it is sufficient to refer to the earlier report. In these instances the reference should be given along with a short comment to refresh the reader's memory. It is better to state the name or kind of method used instead of writing "according to standard methods," or "purified in the usual manner." For instance, it is better to say, "The holothurin hemolysis. . . .", or "According to Planck's theory. . . ." or "The residue was purified in the manner of Nigrelli and Jakowska (3)."

A simplified flow sheet or sketch of the apparatus facing the text is most helpful and often greatly shortens the description. See Appendix B, Figure 5. The discussion should be clear and to the point, omitting operational methods other than the one under consideration.

Whenever the subject matter becomes involved and tends to include many details which, though essential for a successful repetition of the experiment, would be unnecessary for the general account of the investigation, these details should constitute a separate appendix. Appendixes should be lettered consecutively (in capital letters) and references should be made to them at all points where the reader might profitably use them.

Sometimes it may be desirable, however, to insert sections in fine print or indented or otherwise set apart giving the experimental details of procedure, in order to present a single straightforward account. In this way experimental details may be kept close to the more general statements based upon them, yet the reader may pass over the fine print, if he wishes, without inconvenience.

In describing experimental work, chronological order may occasionally provide the best presentation. Procedure manuals and manufacturing processes are chronological, and rightly so. The reader can follow the process step by step better if the work is described in complete chronological order.

In most situations, however, the order in which the experiments were performed is not the most logical. For example, after making a series of runs, perhaps to show the effects of a single variable, a few "fill-in" runs were made. Here it is preferable to present the information in orderly sequence, such as the change in the principal variable.

Report accomplishment!

The emphasis should be placed on the success, the failures, the accuracy, the errors, the potential, the limitations. The reader should be guided through the logic of the work, not the chronology.

A study of the experimental sections of the particular journal for which the article is intended will give the author an idea of the general format and detail acceptable. Industrial reports generally have a very detailed experimental section. R and D (Research and Development) directors know that the more know-how available in any problem, the less time and money needs to be spent on the next related problem. Thesis writing is detailed. But because of space limitations journal writing is "cut to the bone"—brief and concise. The author makes every effort to clarify the work for the reader, but does not waste his time.

Inadequate detail for reports	Detail for reports
Phosphorylase activity was determined on liver homogenates.	Phosphorylase activity was determined on liver samples which had been frozen in a liquid nitrogen-cooled isopentane bath immediately after removal from the perfusion apparatus. The frozen samples then were pulverized in a stainless steel mortar and pestle, maintained about $-70°C$ in an ethanol-dry-ice bath. Aliquots of pulverized frozen liver were homogenized in a solution containing 0.15 M potassium chloride and 0.1 M sodium fluoride and brought to a final dilution of 1:10. The phosphorylase activities of the homogenates were assayed in the direction of glycogen formation by the method described by Cori (1943)[7].

Experimental Results. The results obtained should be presented in full detail, making use of tables, graphs, and photographs. Remarks made previously about the value of appendixes in reducing bulk and increasing readability apply equally well here. Often results are anomalous, but they should not be omitted simply for this reason. On the contrary, it is of particular importance to include them, since even an honest and sincere worker is far more likely to forget results which conflict with his theories or conclusions than those which agree with them. Results known to be invalidated by errors often may be discarded. However, if doubt exists about the source of the error the results should be used, mentioning (without apology) the existence of the error. The detail here again must be adequate so that the reader will obtain all the pertinent technical information he can reasonably expect to find.

Inadequate detail	Detail for reports
The melting point was the same for the unknown sample as the known sample.	The melting point of a mixture of the unknown sample (mp 102-103°) with the known sample (mp 102-102.5°) obtained from Dr. A. B. Crown was 102-103°C.

The writer must not use incomplete sentences in discussing his experimental results.

Incomplete: These correspond to average probabilities of reaction collision. Range 0.1 to 0.5. This is in accordance with model of hot hydrogen-atom.

Complete: These correspond to average probabilities of reaction collision in the range of 0.1 to 0.5. Such high collision efficiencies are in complete accordance with the model of hot hydrogen-atom reactions.

Discussion

It is often desirable to enlarge and discuss the results and specific conclusions, item by item. Reference may be made to the author's own opinion, which, although not proved sufficiently to be listed as conclusions, may have developed as a result of the work done. A discussion of the results and their agreement with previous work on the subject should be included.

If, in carrying out the work, it was discovered that somewhere the planning or execution was faulty, this should be pointed out as a guide for future workers in the field, who might otherwise repeat the errors.

This is the part of the report which is the connecting link between the factual data and the writer's conclusions. The reader is led through the reasoning necessary to reach the conclusions and to see that they are sound. Often it is important to consider opposing contentions and show how the data prove otherwise. But beware of working with statistics. Remember the statistician who was drowned when he tried to wade across a river with an average depth of $3\frac{1}{2}$ feet.

Care should be exercised neither to insult the reader's intelligence with a long discussion of obvious platitudes, nor to assume that the reader agrees with a concept unless it is generally accepted. Judgment is required to strike a good balance without boring the reader, leaving him doubtful, or making him study the data exhaustively to evaluate the reasoning. The author must keep in mind that simple, straightforward statements are most easily understood. The discussion should lead the reader directly to the conclusions.

Typical functions of the concluding paragraphs of scientific papers include (1) future plans, (2) summarization, (3) statement of specific conclusions, (4) presentation of recommendations, and (5) graceful termination. For a particular paper, the objective may be any one of any combination of these.

Future Plans

Future plans for additional work on the general subject or in related fields frequently constitute a good concluding paragraph to the discussion or may be given in a separate section. Often a report covers a major phase of a large investigation, in which case it is helpful to outline future work, possibly already started.

The "Future Plans" section of a report provides a unique opportunity to display creative and imaginative thinking. An opportunity to describe the obvious or the obscure can be handled in almost any way the author desires. Whether he is timid or bold, colorful or bland, imaginative or dull, the author can be disclosed in this rather often ignored section. If the results of the work being reported are part of a much larger picture of work under way and to be done, this section can be used to synthesize the necessary steps to develop the ultimate end result. Care should be exercised to avoid wool-gathering or day-dreaming. Realistically attainable aims, however, should be developed here with justification in the form of references, reasonable projections, and the correlation of current theories.

The "Future Plans" section is the opportunity to portray the effect the work reported will or can have upon the over-all program of the institution or discipline.

Conclusions and Recommendations

Many report readers are more interested in the conclusions interpreted from the results of the test or experiment than in how the work was done. Therefore, it is imperative that the conclusions be complete, concise, and definite. There is sometimes an erroneous tendency to list results as conclusions.

General conclusions drawn from the findings should be repeated in the same order as the findings on which they are based. The conclusions should distinguish clearly between factual trends and the inferences drawn therefrom. When writing the conclusions, the author should put himself in the place of the reader who is not familiar with the subject of the report and try to answer the questions such a reader will ask. Conclusions and recommendations should be so clearly stated that they are capable of but one interpretation. Occasionally a report is written for record purposes only, and no conclusions are required. In such cases a statement to that effect may be made in place of conclusions.

If there is no valid conclusion or recommendation, do not attempt to devise one, but be sure a genuine conclusion is not being overlooked, as most work of value will support one or more valid conclusions.

It is easy to remember that a conclusion is the writer's opinion based on the data presented, whereas a recommendation is the writer's advice regarding what should be done, again based on the data presented. Neither a conclusion nor a recommendation should be confused with a simple and readily apparent observation. Thus, saying "The F-1 and F-2 octane ratings are 89 and 72" is merely an apparent observation. But, saying "Because of the wide spread in F-1 and F-2 octane ratings, the fuel should have good rich-mixture performance," is a real conclusion—the writer's considered opinion based on the data.

The "Conclusions and Recommendations" sections expose the investigator's thinking ability as opposed to the "Results" section, which represents his technique for doing. Any skilled worker can conduct a technical piece of work successfully and promptly, but the importance and meaning of the job can never be seen on the face of a meter dial. It comes from the brain of the technical man. Relations, correlations, anomalies, and logical derivations represent the real results of a technical study. These should be described in these sections.

Summary

The summary usually appears at the end of the report. It should include:

(1) Introductory thought, the problem or question, and the importance of the work, i.e., a summary of the introduction.

(2) What was done and how.

(3) The salient results.

Summarization is the major function in a purely informational paper, that is, one which presents neither formal conclusions nor recommendations for subsequent action.

The concluding summary resembles an abstract in that it presents in condensed, concise form the principal facts or ideas developed or elaborated in the paper. It differs importantly from an abstract, in that it is a part of something instead of being complete in itself; the summary will not appear separate from the rest of the paper, and it is not supposed to be able to stand alone.

There is no need for justification of the validity of the data in the summary. Reference to an easily found chart is permissible, if the chart is the best way to express results. A short tabulation, however, is preferable, and avoid a series of sentences where a short insert table would make the meaning more concise.

Acknowledgments

If the author received other than routine assistance in the work being reported, it is proper to acknowledge this assistance in a paragraph which follows the summary or concluding section of the report under a principal heading, "Acknowledgments." Acknowledgment of analytical work and other help of this nature is not always necessary, but sometimes may be desirable. Simple appreciation is in good taste; lavish, extreme approbation lacks sincerity. It is customary to acknowledge financial support such as, "This work was supported by the U.S. Atomic Energy Commission," in a footnote to the title. Some journals prefer even this type of acknowledgment at the end of the report. When statements, tables, or figures are borrowed from published material, written permission from the copyright owner must be obtained, and acknowledged in the article. It is courteous to ask the author and editor, even if material is not copyrighted. Copyright owners sometimes specify phrasing for credit lines.

Appendix

The preparation of an appendix is necessary if there is added matter which is not essential to the completeness of the manuscript, but which is related to the discussion presented in the body of the report.

The appendix should be treated as a major section of the report with consecutive page numbers and table-of-contents reference. Exhibits or lengthy derivations, to which reference is made in the text but which are not necessary to understanding the objective of the manuscript, may be placed in this section to make them readily available. It is also permissible to include in the appendix tables and graphs which are so numerous or so extensive that they would disturb continuity of thought when the report is read.

If there is more than one division of the appendix, each division should be designated as a separate appendix and should have its own title following the appendix designation of "Appendix A," "Appendix B," etc. The same rules for writing should be used in the preparation of both the main body of the manuscript and the appendix.

Index

The index should not be confused with the table of contents. An index is an alphabetical listing with page numbers or other means of reference of all topics, subjects, phrases, and names mentioned in the report. By custom the index is always the final section of the report.

Seldom is an index prepared for a typewritten report or for any report of limited circulation. A report written for general circulation should contain an index if readers are likely to use the report for frequent reference. Many reports fail to give full value because of the lack of an index or because of not having an adequate one.

The preparation of an index is a difficult and painstaking process, to be undertaken only by one who is familiar with the subject as well as with the steps in indexing. (See Appendix E)

The objective in preparing an index for a report is primarily to see that all subjects and their subdivisions are indexed. It is a process of classification. The procedure may be handled by first carefully reading through the report and marking with colored underline all items that are to be indexed. Subentries may be indicated at the same time by use of a different colored underline. When all words are underlined, the words and their corresponding page numbers are written on 3 x 5 cards. The next step is to sort the cards into alphabetical order by main entries and subentries. The final step is to type the listing in suitable typographical arrangement. The final typing should be verified by checking the original colored markings in the report with the typed index.*

G. V. Carey, President of the Society of Indexers, says, "The true aim of an indexer is to be methodical rather than mechanical, and the best indexer is he who is most generously endowed with

---

* A book that thoroughly covers the methods used in indexing is: Collison, Robert, "Indexing Books," John de Graff, Inc., New York, 1962. Another good book is: Carey, G. V., "Making an Index," 3rd ed., Cambridge University Press, London, 1963.

common sense. The author, unless incorrigibly slipshod or absent-minded, *ought* to be the best indexer of his own work.

"There is a saying quoted by a seventeenth-century bibliographer that the index of a book should be made by the author, even if the book itself be written by someone else. Whether or not intended to be merely witty, it has an element of truth; but it is a counsel of perfection. Though almost any book could be indexed more efficiently, and with less trouble, by its own author than by anyone else, there are far too many authors unwilling to shoulder the task."

Indexing is not the same to all people. Indexing of reports and classifying books for retrieval purposes by librarians and other information specialists supplies road signs for the retrieval of documents. Their job is more exacting and much more complex than preparing an index to a book. Indexing a book is the preparation of road signs for the retrieval of pages within the bounds of the book's cover.

The librarians' bibliographic reference is the book authors' page number. The authority list, thesaurus, or classification system of the librarians is simply the vocabulary of the author.

Although many of the principles are the same for the two operations called "indexing," an author with persistence and care can do an adequate job of report indexing. But the task of subject heading assignment for classifying an author's book as it enters the hierarchy of mankind's stored knowledge should always be left to the professional.

Generalized Report Outline

(1) The *title* suggests the contents of the report.

(2) The *table of contents* lists all the division and subdivision headings of the report.

(3) The *abstract,* not part of the paper, is an adjunct intended to convey briefly the content of the paper.

(4) The *introduction* contains the identification of the report objectives.

(5) The *body* consists of the detailed answers to the questions raised in the introduction.

(6) The *discussion* is the connecting link between the factual data and the writer's conclusions.

(7) The *conclusions and recommendations* interpret the answers given in the body of the report.

(8) The *future plans* represent further steps necessary to accomplish some larger objective.

(9) The *summary* reviews the whole report briefly.

(10) The *acknowledgments* list the nonroutine help received in performing the work being reported.

(11) The *references* or *bibliography* should contain a numbered list of publications mentioned or quoted in the report.

(12) The *tables* and *figures* are used to illustrate important aspects carefully presented.

(13) The *appendixes* contain an extended discussion of special points mentioned in the report.

(14) The *index* classifies the subject matter of the report in alphabetical order.

The vitality of the report is centered in the results obtained from the author's study or experimental work.

CHAPTER 5 *Tables and Illustrations*

The vitality of the report is centered in the results obtained from the author's study or experimental work. He must present his information in a form designed to convince the reader that his conclusions are correct. Therefore, it is important not to cloud the real issues with extraneous information. For example, extensive data may have been taken in connection with a series of experiments. Every effort may have been made to hold constant all conditions except one, and hence the study represents the effect of the one variable on product quality. The salient data are, therefore, the changes in product quality related to the change in the one variable along with merely the average values maintained for the other variables. This information is sufficient for the text. The detailed data for all the conditions should be placed in the appendix.

In preparing charts and tables, consistent units should be used throughout. Do not plot a curve in degrees Fahrenheit and refer to the function elsewhere in degrees centigrade. Units should be chosen to conform to those normally used with the subject and by principal readers. In general, metric units should be selected for highly technical work and English units for plant or development problems. Many engineers are adopting metric units, which is the desirable standard of measurement.

Except in such recognized conventions as cc/gal of tetraethyl lead, never use mixed units. Also, avoid the use of such units as gal/100 ft^2/14.5 in. of height; instead, use gal/ft^2/ft. If it is highly convenient for the sake of an immediate comparison to use an unusual set of units, the conventional expression also should be included.

Abbreviations should be clear and conventional. See Appendix A for a list of abbreviations which is the latest (March 1963) approved list of the American Institute of Physics. The abbreviations in this list are so common that they may be used without explanation. No periods are used except in special cases noted. Abbreviations of units are written in the same way for the singular and the plural. Abbreviations of units and the symbol for percent (%) are used only when preceded by a numeral.

Tables

If for brevity in a table it is necessary to "coin" an abbreviation, or if the reader may not recognize it, use a letter or asterisk and footnote, but for a series of footnotes successive letters are more readable. Numerals for footnote references in tables must never be used because of the danger of confusion with the data.

The author should not use more than four or five lines of tabular material without making it a numbered table with a title. Otherwise makeup is confusing and this increases production costs.

Tables should be prepared with the realization that they will be typed. The author should bear in mind the limitations of a typewriter and have consideration for the typist. He should not expect a nontechnical typist to interpret technical data and suitably organize the table. Frequently, it is better to prepare a hand-lettered tracing when the tabular data do not lend themselves to convenient typing. When possible, tables should be arranged so that they appear on 8½ by 11 in. or 8 by 10 in. paper in the normal reading position. Too frequently a table is laid out 12 columns wide and 3 rows deep, whereas it would be just as clear and much better in appearance if prepared 3 columns wide and 12 rows deep. Large tables often may have to be reduced from their original size by photography; therefore the lettering must be large enough to be readable after reduction.

Typical tables are shown in Appendix B. In each table a different style for giving information is shown. Table I is an illustration of how a simple device may be used to emphasize data. The data in the box show that hydroquinone monobenzoate was the most effective of the additives tested. Emphasis may also be obtained by use of color. Table II was originally prepared on an 11 by 17 in. page and reduced to fit the 6 by 9 in. page.

Tables originally larger than 11 by 17 in. are not legible enough when reduced to fit a typewritten report on 8½ by 11 in. paper. Such tables may be reduced to 11 by 17 in. and folded for inclusion in a report. A table larger than 22 by 34 in., however, cannot be reduced to 11 by 17 in. and still be legible.

These tables and figures in Appendix B were copied from a report published by Tennessee Eastman Company, Kingsport, Tennessee.*

Tables should state clearly in the titles and notes the source, applicability, and scope of the data so that the tables are clear by themselves if they should become separated from the report.

Since tables (and illustrations) generally are not studied in detail except by those readers most directly concerned, the text should abstract from the table (or illustration) enough information to ensure the reader's appreciation of its significance. This textual material should be coherent enough to stand alone without need for close study of the table.

In referring to a table or figure in the text, always refer to a specific table, for example: "See Table VII," not "See the following table," or "The data in Table III prove...." or "Table V shows ...." or "The results (see Table XI p. 35) indicate...." Then the text can be continued wherever possible while typing or typesetting, regardless of the exact position of the table in the manuscript. And if mention is made again many pages removed, the page on which the table or figure appears should be given.

A table (or illustration) should be placed as near as possible to the first point in the text where it is mentioned. If it is small enough, or can be sufficiently reduced, it should be displayed on the page with the text. This integral relationship to the text should be emphasized by placing it to allow some text to precede and some to

* McMahon, E. M., Bridwell, R. S., Cassell, G. S., and West, M., *Preparation of Technical Reports and Papers,* Sept., 1962.

follow it. If it is so large that such display would crowd out too much of the text, it should be placed on a page by itself following the page from which reference to it is first made (or on the page opposite when a report is typed on both sides).

Care should be taken to choose the captions (column headings) and the stubs (left column) in such a way that only figures appear in the body of the table; thus, the captions and stubs will include all unit designations. Occasionally, however, it is desirable to prepare a table in which words rather than figures appear in one or more of the columns, or both words and figures might appear as in Table II, Appendix B. Principal words in both the captions and the stub should be capitalized. The unit designation should be set off from the captions or stub by a comma and should not be capitalized. Column headings should be separated from the column by a line.

Body columns should be aligned by the decimal point. In numbers less than 1, a zero should always precede the decimal, i.e., 0.537.

Using a power of 10 in a column heading, such a "pressure, mm $\times$ 10^{-3}," should be avoided since it is not clear whether the numbers in the column have been or *are to be* multiplied by 10^{-3}. To avoid misunderstanding, a factor such as 10^{-3} should be directly associated with a number, not with a descriptive term such as "mm." For example:

(pressure, mm)		(pressure, 10^{-3} mm)		(pressure, mm $\times$ 10^{-3})
13.6×10^{-3}	or	13.6	not	13.6
1.46×10^{-3}		1.46		1.46
119.0×10^{-3}		119.0		119.0
6.40×10^{-3}		6.40		6.40

It is possible in many cases where the metric system is used to eliminate the power of 10 in the number by changing the units. In the above example, if "microns" were used as the unit rather than "mm," the need for a power of 10 is eliminated. If there is any chance that the meaning of a heading will be misunderstood, a footnote should be used with the table to make the meaning clear.

Vertical rulings may be used in tables if desired. However, all tables in a report should be consistent, rulings in each table or no vertical lines in any. The table should contain all pertinent data as well as useful totals, ratios, and arrays.

If the table will not fit in the normal reading position, it should be arranged with the title at the binding edge of the normal right hand page. Large tables beginning on the left hand or back of the page should be arranged with the title at the opposite or leading edge of the paper. Such a rule permits uniformity among typists and typesetters and permits the next logical extension of the large table. In this case, the table begins at the leading edge of the left-hand page and continues across the binding down to the leading edge of the right-hand page.

In cases where large tables are properly more broad than long, they should be arranged on two facing pages with the title across the normal top edge. In the latter case, box lines and titles should be continued across each sheet, through the center of the binding and where possible, the first column should be repeated at the extreme right of the table for easier reading.

All tables should be numbered consecutively (in Roman numerals placed *above* the table), to be followed in the next line by a complete title with the first letter of each important word capitalized. Unwieldy titles are to be avoided. If a title must carry more information than can be fitted neatly into a caption, a portion of the information is given after the title or as a subtitle on the next line, with the first letter of each important word capitalized. It is important that tables should be capable of standing by themselves. To create this, columns should be labeled specifically. However, brevity in column headings is desirable and abbreviations should be used freely.

Frequently in a table it is necessary to repeat numbers one under the other. Ditto marks are not recommended for this purpose; repeat the numbers or incorporate the repeated numbers in the column heading. However, when no data are available, dashes may be used.

To achieve effectiveness of tabular presentation, the material should be written and revised with the same sharp scrutiny that is given to the text. Particular attention should be given to proofreading data, since transcription errors are easy to make but hard to find. Less manhours are used if two people proofread tabular data; one reading aloud to the other is fast and accurate. Some generalities that are helpful in designing tables are given below.*

(1) When four or more items of data are given, they should be presented in tabular form. Tabulating the data makes the information much easier to understand.

(2) The same unit of measurement should be used for comparable properties or dimensions.

(3) The units of measurement used in a table should all be of the same system, such as metric, English, or apothecary.

(4) If an item is repeated several times in a table, probably it should appear just once in the title, in a footnote, or in a column or row head. Often such repetition obscures important similarities.

(5) Column and row headings should be used to group related data.

(6) In a table reporting a series of experiments or tests with some factors constant for certain groups and other factors varying, the data should be grouped according to the constant factors when possible.

(7) Usually the chronological order in which data were obtained is of little importance and the sequence of the data in the table should be determined by more significant factors.

(8) Footnotes should be referred to in sequence, line by line, from left to right, across the entire table.

(9) Often only a summary table should be presented in the main body of a report, and the supporting or record tables should be placed in an appendix.

A table should be prepared so that it:

(1) Is complete in itself.

(2) Contains only closely related facts.

(3) Has a concise but descriptive title.

(4) Makes discussion concerning it easy to follow.

(5) Contains any footnotes essential to clarity.

(6) When feasible, contains reference numbers rather than notebook and page numbers.

* From E. Cortelyou's paper, which is a classic ,"Some Fundamentals of Designing Tables of Data," *J. Chem. Educ.* **31,** 590 (1954).

Figures

A figure is a general term used to denote illustrations of any character other than tables. It may be a chart, graph, form, blueprint, photograph, sketch, or line drawing. All figures in a report should be numbered consecutively in Arabic numerals *beneath* the figure, together with a complete legend that will indicate the significance of the figure without making it necessary to refer to the text.

No matter how many well-chosen words appear in a report, no matter how forceful or carefully written it may be, its appeal and readability can be enhanced by graphic arrangement. A report is most inviting to its reader when its graphic arrangement and its illustrations beckon to him as an aid in his reading.

There is a world of contrast between an easy-to-read report, with good illustrations, and the dull appearance of its graphically uninviting counterpart, even though both may contain the same words. Good design, however, must start with the author. The author may be furnished with excellent editorial help and graphic aids. *His* basic choices and decisions, if not well-conceived, can nullify the best efforts of the publications specialists who try to help him.

There are many books and articles dealing with the word design of reports, but there is very little advice devoted to their graphic design. Two reasons for this: (1) graphic design is a difficult and diverse subject, not lending itself to uniform analysis, and (2) illustrative material is sometimes left to an editor as a polishing job—something that the author need not fuss with. But in order to fully analyze and understand his own data he ought to fuss with it.

When an author neglects the appearance of his report, he loses the opportunity to control one of the best selling devices he can employ. Visual appeal may be the one compelling feature that lifts his report above so many others that compete for the reader's attention.*

Graphs make up the largest class of figures. To be effective, a graph must show the reader in a matter of seconds the general relationship of all the variables shown. For this reason it is generally

---

* A short, but good, report on figures for technical reports is: Gregory, J. E., "How to Improve Your Figure," *STWP Review* 10(3), 12 (1963).

poor practice to include more than three curves of correlations on one graph; four may be used if the result does not appear crowded; but never five (see Appendix B, Figures 1 and 2 for examples of line graphs. Sometimes color can be used to identify curves that are too close together to differentiate readily by variation of line styles. Even though very effective, the use of color is expensive and generally not used in the technical journals, but it is used in some industrial reports.

A flow diagram can use color effectively in following the flow of materials through a system.

Some graphs have only one central idea presented; the title is brief but sufficiently descriptive; the figure is uncrowded; congestion on the axes is avoided by numbering alternate scale-interval points; the letter height, size and style of data point symbols, and line width provide good legibility (see Figure 3 in Appendix B).

Standard line styles and the use of a single axis to plot both positive and negative values can be used. In this graph the data points can be omitted because the object is to show relations, not actual data, as in Figure 4, Appendix B. Coordinate scales should be chosen and labeled with care so that the maximum amount of information may be obtained from the graph with a minimum of interpolation.

A useful help in preparing graphs and illustrations is the pamphlet "A Guide for Preparing Technical Illustrations for Publication and Projection." *

Every effort should be made to confine graphs to 8½ by 11 in. or 8 by 10 in. page size; if this is impossible, the drawings should be photographically reduced or prepared so that pages are report size on one side and will fold out in only one direction. The same margins should be used for graphs as for text, particularly at the binding edge.

Graphs, the chief class of figures, should be prepared according to the following principles which are suggested in "Preparation of Technical Reports and Papers." †

* American Society of Mechanical Engineers, 345 East 47 St., New York. N.Y.

† McMahon, E. M., Bridwell, R. S., Cassell, G. S., and West, M., Tennessee Eastman Co., Research Laboratories, Kingsport, Tenn., Sept., 1962.

(1) The number of words should be limited by using
   (a) Brief captions for the axes.
   (b) Standard abbreviations.
   (c) Explanatory notes only when essential.

(2) The title should
   (a) Indicate what the figure is intended to show, not consist merely of a repetition of the axes captions.
   (b) Be concise yet sufficiently descriptive.

(3) The axes should be presented
   (a) Using ordinarily only the abscissa (horizontal axis) and the left-hand ordinate.
   (b) With the caption for the ordinate written horizontally.
   (c) With only the necessary scale-interval points numbered. The scales chosen should be easily readable, not 3 divisions for 4 units. A good rule is to make the smallest scale division a decimal value of 1, 2, or 5.
   (d) With grid lines replaced by short lines drawn inside the axes.
   (e) With a heavy or colored grid line at the zero point if both positive and negative values are shown. Negative values appear below a horizontal zero line and to the left of a vertical zero line.
   (f) With the dependent variable on the ordinate (Y axis) and the independent variable on the abscissa (horizontal or X axis).

(4) The curves should be
   (a) Drawn without including data points unless they are essential.
   (b) Drawn using standard symbols for data points that must be included:
      ○, ●, △, ▲, □, ■.
   (c) Drawn using standard line styles:
      (——), (- - - -), (— - — - — -), (— — —), (— - - - —).
   (d) Limited to those essential to the report; the maximum should be four.

(e) Identified, if possible, by horizontal labels.

(f) Separated widely enough to be distinct.

(g) Shown in color, if necessary, to differentiate data or provide emphasis.

(h) Chosen so that the minimum scale division does not express the function far more precisely than warranted, for example, 3.01 letters per word.

(i) Drawn so that the trend of one or more functions is not unduly magnified or minimized. For instance, poor choice of a scale can make a change of a tenth of an octane number in gasoline blending appear as a marked peak. If there are two or more graphs with one variable in a given report, e.g., octane number plotted against several operating conditions, the scale for the variable should be consistent throughout. If not, one operating condition may appear to have much more marked effect on the variable than the others where such is not the case at all.

The author should keep in mind that his report is not just a recounting of data, but a bridge from his own understanding to that of his reader.

Photographs

Before ordering or taking a photograph the author should be sure it is the most effective means of illustrating a point. For instance, machinery and process detail are helpful, but pictures of trucks, ships, freight cars, and miscellaneous products are usually not necessary. A test for an illustration is, "Does it help to explain the subject matter?" If it does not, it should be left out. In many cases a simple schematic diagram or sketch will be better than a photograph for the purpose. Cropping sometimes eliminates distracting elements.

Appropriate labels (call-outs) may be included in the photograph for identification or to provide explanatory information relative to the photograph. If call-outs might help the photograph, the advice of a good photographer should be sought for the proper mechanics.

Photographs are numbered consecutively in Arabic numerals beneath the picture. A title should be attached to each print or negative. In the case of photomicrographs, if it is necessary to change the size of the original, the caption must note the change in magnification.

Some reports use only black-and-white photography while others may be permtited to use the more expensive color photography. It is best to check the journal the report is going to be submitted to before taking a number of color photos. Also it is a good idea for an author to check with his supervisor or advisor in the event the report is for industrial or academic purposes. The author submits one (generally 8 by 10 in.) glossy print or negative of each photograph with the manuscript; a glossy print is preferred.

Sometimes it is advantageous to include in a photograph a ruler or some other familiar object to show the relative size of the object being described. Detail and contrast is important; also retouching may be desirable to increase clarity and give emphasis. The author can use cropping to eliminate distracting elements, or outlining to accentuate an important bypass pipe, or a neutral tone to deemphasize items of lesser importance.

The characteristics of a good photograph are: brief title, but sufficiently descriptive, uncluttered background; only essential parts of the equipment are shown and these parts are labeled.

Drawings

All drawings must serve the reader of the report, but as in the selection of text material, it is better to include doubtful illustrations rather than omit something a reader might want. The author too often overestimates the readers' understanding of the subject.

In the description of apparatus, it will nearly always be desirable to have a sketch of the apparatus. This sketch should be schematic. As a rule it should give more detail than a flow diagram but not as much as a drawing intended for machine shop use, as seen in Figure 5, Appendix B.

High standards with respect to any of these graphic aids contribute immeasurably to clarity, and often a single, carefully prepared diagram will save pages of words.

The author is responsible for obtaining written permission to use copyrighted illustrations that will aid his report. Courtesy demands a credit line for any illustration not the author's.

Some generalities that are helpful in designing any type illustration are:

(1) The author's name and the figure number is noted in the margin or on the back of every figure submitted for duplication to avoid being misplaced.

(2) Illustrations included in a report appendix should be numbered in the same sequence with those in the text.

(3) Footnotes to figures should be indicated by letters rather than by numbers.

(4) In an organization chart, the highest authority should be placed at the top, and, if possible, those beneath should be placed so that all which fall at the same level of importance will be on the same level on the page.

CHAPTER 6 *References*

It is traditional in writing to make specific reference to source material selected from the works of others. In technical and scientific writing it is especially desirable to give exact and complete references to all works that are mentioned or quoted.* This practice is fair to the original author, the writer, and the reader. The assistance to the reader who may wish to read further on the subject or to look up additional details of the work cited must not be overlooked. To show that the literature of the field has been studied also establishes prestige and confidence in the report.

In a terminal bibliography, a reference should appear no more than once, and, no matter how many times the reference is cited in the text, the same reference number should be used for this entry. In the footnote system, a reference may be repeated with a different footnote letter if a citation would otherwise direct to a footnote too many pages removed.

In an extensive work with many sections, it may be convenient (and will certainly be more flexible) to provide each section with its own terminal bibliography or with its own set of footnotes. In this kind of arrangement, numbering or lettering is started anew in every section. The appearance of a reference in one section is then, independent of its appearance in any other section.

Footnotes

Footnotes, if they need to be used, should be indicated by an asterisk in the text (or letters in sequence if more than one occurs

---

* A thoughtful discussion on authorship in references is: Wendt, G. R., "Coauthors and Gentlemen," *Science* 145, 110-112 (1964).

on a page). The note is single-spaced, indented two spaces from the asterisk, placed three spaces below the last line of the text on the page and is sometimes separated from this main body of the text by a hairline rule. If a long footnote which must continue from one page to the next is unavoidable, it should begin on the page where reference to it occurs. The arrangement should be such that the note will break in the middle of a sentence and conclude on the next page, where it takes precedence over the footnotes for that page.

Normally footnotes will not appear in a report. These remarks should either appear in parentheses in the text, be collected under "Notes and References," or be in the appendix. In printed matter such as brochures, bulletins, and books, footnotes are frequently found.

Source References

Primary sources (patents, technical reports, dissertations, theses, and original papers in journals) are generally preferred and are used more than secondary source references (*Beilstein's Handbuch, Chemical Abstracts, Index Medicus, Physical Reviews,* textbooks, encyclopedias, etc.). However, these secondary sources are acceptable in many cases.

Source references ought to be given whenever quotations, ideas, or results of other authors are used or mentioned. The name of the author (or when the name is omitted, the idea) is followed by a number in parentheses or superscript. For example:

(1) This was achieved in the case of aldolase (8).
(2) Crick (14) carried this to the random coil level.
(3) Tinoco, Halpern, and Simpson [23] found. . . .

Never reference a heading; a heading is merely a guide to the text. The reference number should appear in the first sentence of the paragraph or section where a previously published topic is discussed at length. For example:

In order to be useful the references should be exact and should be written in a uniform style.[7]

Note that when a punctuation mark comes at the same place as the reference number the superscript number is inserted *after* and the number in parentheses *before* the punctuation.

The reference numbers refer to a numbered bibliography which follows the acknowledgment. Most bibliographies are arranged chronologically as they appear in the text and a few (for example: *Cancer*) alphabetically by senior author. If no author is shown, the title should be used for arrangement. Generally in an industrial report the references are arranged chronologically. An author should study the arrangement used in the particular journal he wishes to submit his paper to, and follow that style.

Authors and editors have resisted standardization in reference style. Capitalization, order, abbreviation, and punctuation in technical references are far from uniform.

Specific references may appear either as footnotes or as a compilation in a terminal bibliography. Footnotes are not suitable for short technical reports but are usually used in dissertations. Dissertations are often reduced to microfilm form and the reader will find it convenient to have the reference given on the same page as the citation. Accordingly, writers whose work might be microfilmed should consider using the footnote system for references. Some scientific and technical journals, such as *Experientia*, use footnotes for documentation. If numbers in parentheses are used for the bibliography, then some journals use the superscript numbers for footnotes in the text, rather than the letters. If no terminal bibliography is used and references appear as footnotes, as in *Experientia*, superscript numbers in a single enumeration cover all footnotes, including references in some journals.

The titles of periodicals in either text or references should be underlined, that is, italicized. The titles of books, papers, chapters, and similar units should be in quotation marks. The capitalization for the titles of books or journals follows the rules of the language in which they are written, or the style of the journal to which the report is being submitted.

These following formats are recommended as simple and familiar.

Books

Show the senior author's name (last name first), and coauthors (last name first), title of book (quotation marks), name of editor or translator when necessary (initials first), edition number when more than one edition of a publication has been printed, name of publisher, place of publication, year of publication, and volume and page numbers of the citation, when necessary, in the order listed.

Several standard series of books have become so familiar that every scientist assumes every other scientist knows and uses them frequently. These are "Inorganic Synthesis," "Biochemical Preparations," "International Critical Tables," "Organic Reactions," and others in the various technical fields. References to such sources are correct when given in the form used for books. For instance:

Field, L. and Clark, R. D., "Organic Syntheses," J. C. Sheehan, ed.-in-chief, John Wiley & Sons, Inc., New York, 1958, Vol. 38, p. 75.

When a translated foreign publication is referred to, it should be included in the reference under the name of the original author and not the translator. The title of a translated work should be followed by the abbreviation "transl. by" and the name of the translator, with the first name or initials first. Other publication data should follow.

If the reference is on microfilm or "Microcard" form, the word "microfilm" or "Microcard" should be placed in parentheses at the end of the reference.

One Author

1. Hadzi, J., "The Evolution of the Metazoa," Macmillan Co., New York, 1963.
2. Groggins, P. H., "Unit Processes in Organic Synthesis," 4th ed., McGraw-Hill Book Co., New York, 1952 (microfilm).

Two Authors

3. Hutchison, T. S. and Baird, D. C., "The Physics of Engineering Solids," John Wiley & Sons, New York, 1963.

Three Authors or More

4. Rossi, B. B., Jones, E. S., and Staub, H. H., "Ionization Chambers and Counters: Experimental Techniques," McGraw-Hill Book Co., New York, 1949, NNES Vol. 2, pp. 190-5.

5. Kimber, D. D., Bray, C. E., and Stackpole, E. E., "Textbook of Anatomy and Physiology," 9th ed., Macmillan Co., New York, 1934.

A reference should include the names of all the authors, and the names should be given in the order of their appearance in the original source. If a paper is worth citing, the least its authors deserve by way of acknowledgment and courteous treatment is mention of their names. Within the body of the text there may be some reason to use *et al.*, and *coworkers, and others,* since a long string of names in the middle of a sentence can blur the sentence thought. But mention of only one of the authors overemphasizes his contribution and takes credit from others, who in many cases did the major portion of the work. A simple rule is to use either all or none of the authors' names in the text.

Authors' initials should be given in the reference; they are not required in the text. However, the abbreviation $M.$ appearing before the author's name in *Comptes rendus* (French Academy of Science) stands for "Monsieur," and $H.$ before an author's name in a German written article stands for "Mr.," not the author's name or initial.

Association as the Author

6. Chemical Abstracts Service, "Directions for Abstractors," Am. Chem. Soc., Ohio State Univ., Columbus, Ohio, 1964, p. 10-6.

7. American Standards Association, "Abbreviations for Use on Drawings," New York, 1962, Bulletin Z32.13, pp. 2-7.

No Author Named

8. "A Manual of Style," 11th ed., Univ. of Chicago Press, Chicago, 1949, p. 150.

9. "Chemical Formulary," Harry Bennett, ed., Chemical Publishing Co., New York, 1933.

Author and Editor

10. Chikazumi, Soshin, "The Physics of Magnetism," Stanley H. Charap, Engl. ed., John Wiley & Sons, New York, 1964.

11. Ephraim, F., "Inorganic Chemistry," P. C. L. Thorne and E. R. Roberts, ed., John Wiley & Sons, Interscience, New York, 1946.

12. Singer, J., "Elements of Numerical Analysis," Ralph P. Goas, Jr., consulting ed., Academic Press, New York, 1964.

Author and Translator

13. Steinberg, J. L. and Lequeux, J., "Radio Astronomy," transl. from Fr. by R. N. Bracewell, McGraw-Hill Book Co., New York, 1963.

14. Karlson, P., "Introduction to Modern Biochemistry," transl. of 3rd Ger. ed., 1962, by C. H. Doering, Academic Press, New York, 1963.

One Volume of a Work of Several Volumes

15. "Newer Methods of Preparative Organic Chemistry," W. Foerst, ed., transl. by F. K. Kirchner, Academic Press, New York, 1963, Vol. II, p. 109.

16. Tou, Julius T., "Optimum Design of Digital Control Systems," Richard Bellman, series ed., Academic Press, New York, 1963, Vol. X of "Mathematics in Science and Engineering."

17. Atteberry, G. C., Auble, J. L., and Hunt, E. F., "Introduction to Social Science," Macmillan Co., New York, 1942, Vol. II.

One Book of a Series

18. Badger, W. L. and McCabe, W. L., "Elements of Chemical Engineering," 2nd ed., Chemical Engineering Series, McGraw-Hill Book Co., New York, 1936, pp. 63-117.

19. Walker, J. F., "Formaldehyde," 3rd ed., ACS Monograph No. 159, Reinhold Pub. Corp., New York, 1964.

When the reference is a standard and very well known secondary source, as the "International Critical Tables," the reference can be simplified:

20. "International Critical Tables," II, 248 (1928).

Sometimes the various chapters in a book or set of books will be written by one or more authors, and the whole book edited by other individuals. If reference is to be given to the author and his chapter, the reference may be given as follows:

21. Bachmann, W. E., "Free Radicals," in "Organic Chemistry," H. Gilman, ed., John Wiley & Sons, New York, 1938, Vol. I, pp. 489-54.

22. Hawley, G. G., "Put Punch in Your Writing," in "Better Report Writing," by W. H. Waldo, Reinhold Pub. Corp., New York, 1957, p. 135.

Surveys have shown that there are more errors per line in a table of references than in any other prose compilation. A study of these errors revealed that authors are more frequently at fault than typists and typographers. Extreme care is required with author spelling (Smyth or Smythe), column and year numbers (Vol. 66, 1964 or Vol. 64, 1966). Meticulous care should be exercised to check citations with their original source. Abstract journals, card catalogs, and particularly other references in other reports are most untrustworthy. Although checking references may be a boring occupation for a busy scientist, consider the reader. He enthusiastically chases down one of the writer's references, which through a typographical error indicated an American journal instead of the correct French one. The volume numbers are reversed, indicating a volume which has not yet been issued, with a wrong page number, which when finally found, is in the middle of an article for the wrong year. For example:

Actual: Smith, A. B. *Physics,* 71 (32), 235 (1916).
Corrected: Smith, A. B. *Physica,* 17 (32), 238 (1961).

Journals or Periodicals

Show the senior author's name (last name first), and coauthors (last name first), title of paper or article if necessary (in quotes), abbreviated name of periodical (italics), series if necessary, volume number (wavy underscore by hand to indicate bold face type), issue number (in parentheses), page numbers, and year of publication (parentheses). No publisher need be mentioned for a periodical reference.

Some journals, such as *Bulletin de la societé chimique de France, Chemistry and Industry,* or *Journal of the Chemical Society,* do not use volume numbers. In bibliographical references to such journals the *year* is placed where the volume number would ordinarily go and is treated like a volume number. The editorial policy of other journals, *Canadian Journal of Chemistry, Journal of the American Chemical Society, Journal of Physical Chemistry,* places the parenthesized year *after* the page number, whether volume numbers are available or not.

In citing articles that are short, the first page of the article is usually given. When the article is over ten pages long, the specific page of reference may be given rather than the first page number. In other cases the first and last page are given for long articles. Locating the specific place of reference in a long article may be burdensome to the reader. In book references the exact page number is always given.

Journal title word abbreviations can be found easily in the back of many style manuals in all the technical and scientific fields. These lists are adapted from The Chemical Abstracts Service list which is easily available and most widely accepted.*

References made to physical journals, especially *in* the physical journals, omit the article in the title, such as, *Transactions of the Faraday Society:*

 1. Richards, R. B., *Trans. Faraday Soc.,* **42,** 10-29 (1946).

The Chemical Abstracts Service adds in parentheses at the end of the reference the abbreviation of the language in which the original article is written. For instance:

 2. Duval, Clement, "Astatine," *Chim. Anal. (Paris),* **45**(11), 557-9 (1963) (Fr).

 3. Johnson, T., "How to Organize Your Writing," *Am. Mach.,* **104**(8), 127-30 (1960) (Eng).

Note there is no period after the language abbreviation.

If there are two authors, the first author's full name should be followed by the word *and* and the second author's name (no comma). If there are three or more authors, their full names should be separated by commas with the word *and* preceding the name of the last author only.

 4. Anzalone, A. M., Brokars, C. A., and Cohn, G., "A Novel Index Tailored to Plastics Specialists," *Am. Doc.,* **15**(3), 191 (1964).

* For the latest issue write to The Chemical Abstracts Service, Ohio State Univ., Columbus, Ohio 43210, and request "A List of Periodicals Abstracted by CAS."

Some industries prefer inclusion of the article's title, but some journals do not include the title in their references.

5. MacMillan, J. T. and Welt, I. D., *Am. Doc.*, 12(1), 27 (1961).

Some journals have no volume number and the year is used instead.

6. Roberts, I., *J. Chem. Soc.*, 1956, 832.

Some journals do not paginate by the year or volume, but by the issue. In this case the date of issue to the day should be mentioned so that the reference can be found easily. For instance:

7. Brown, G. S., *Oil Gas J.*, 54, 113 (Aug. 13, 1956).

An abstract reference or a reference to another readily available secondary source should follow *any* reference in which there is question about the convenient accessibility of the original article, such as patents, or an article in Russian, Japanese, etc.

8. Lal, D., *Proc. Indian Acad. Sci.*, 36A, 75-96 (1952); cf. *CA* 46, 9446a.
9. Robinson, F., Good, C. R., and Sommer, S. (to Hercules Powder Co.), U.S. 3,066,130 (cl. 260-94.9), Nov. 27, 1962; Ger. Appl. Oct. 8, 1955; 2 pp.; cf. *CA*, 56, 788a.

If only the abstract is used the journal reference should appear second.

10. Panizzi, L. and Nicolaus, R. A., *CA*, 45, 3812j; *Gazz. chim. ital.*, 80, 431 (1950).

If a series number is necessary in a reference it is given this way:

11. Smith, A. W., *Trans. Roy. Soc. Can.*, *Sect. III* [4] 1, 403-14 (1963).

Ibid., Op. Cit., and Other Latin Words

Unnecessary repetition in footnotes or bibliographical references is avoided by using *op. cit.*, *loc. cit.*, *ibid.*, and *idem*. The first two (*op. cit.*, for *opere citato*, "in the work cited," and *loc. cit.*, for *locature citato*, "in the place cited") may be used only when accompanied by an author's name. This name may be either in the text with the reference number after it or at the beginning of the foot-note. When a book or a journal article is cited, the full reference should be given the first time it is referred to, and sometimes, for the convenience of readers, the first time it is referred to in each section of the report. In later references *op. cit.* or *loc. cit.*, with or without a page reference, may replace the full reference.

First Reference

1. Price, D. J. de S., "Little Science, Big Science," Columbia Univ. Press, New York, 1963, pp. 94-115.

Later Reference

2. Price, D. J. de S., *op. cit.*, p. 14.

First Reference

1. Strahler, A. N., "The Earth Sciences," Harper and Row, New York, 1963, p. 92.

Later Reference.

2. Strahler, A. N., *loc. cit.*

Or if "Strahler [3]" appears in the text, the name need not be repeated.

3. *Loc. cit.*

Note that *op. cit.* cannot be used if more than one book by the same author has been cited.

The abbreviation ibid., for *ibidem,* "in the same place," may be used when reference is made to the same work referred to above or in the preceding footnote on the same or the opposite page. Some writers use *ibid.* to refer to the preceding note in the list.

First Reference

1. Weinstein, E. A. and Spry, J., *Am. Doc.,* 15(3), 185-95 (1964).

Any Later Reference

2. Weinstein, E. A. and Spry, J., *op. cit.*, p. 190.

Immediately following either of the two above:

3. *Ibid.*, p. 187.

Identical with the preceding note:

4. *Ibid.*

Ibid. is understood to replace all words that are identical in consecutive notes. For example:

1. *Brit. Doc.,* 1954, Vol. IV(257), 286.
2. *Ibid.,* (260), 201. (*Ibid.* stands for *Brit. Doc.,* Vol. IV.)
3. *Ibid.,* 290. [*Ibid.* stands for *Brit. Doc.,* Vol. IV(260).]
4. Barr, G. C. and Butler, J. A. V., *Biochem. J.* **88,** 252-9 (1963), cf. *ibid.,* 176-82.

The Latin word *idem* is occasionally used in footnotes to refer to the same person or reference as the preceding one. It should, however, not be used in reports because there is no common agreement on its use.

Reports

Show the senior author's name (last name first), and coauthors (last name first), title of the report (quotes), issuing and originating agencies, date of publication, document number (parenthesized), and page number, if necessary, in the order listed. For examples:

1. Marshall, E. D. and Rickard, R. R., "Spectrophotometric Determination of Rhodium," Carbide and Carbon Chem. Div., K-25 Plant, Feb. 14, 1965 (K-3986).
2. Baker, W. H., "Counting Systems for Pulses of Wide Dynamic Range," Monsanto Research Corp., Mound Lab., Oct. 21, 1964 (MLM-8165), p. 5.
3. Northwest Electrodevelopment Staff, "Zirconium: Its Production and Properties," U.S. Bur. Mines Bull., 1956 (561), pp. 70-90.
4. American Standards Association, "Letter Symbols for Chemical Engineering," ASA, 1955 (Y10.12).
5. American Chemical Society, "Hints to Authors," Washington, D.C., 1961 (Am. Chem. Soc. Bull. 12).
6. Industrial Engineering Division, "Instructions for Preparing Formal Reports on Investigation and Experimental Work," E. I. duPont de Nemours and Co., Reissued Jan., 1964 (ED-7414).

Many of the BIOS (British Intelligence Objectives Subcommittee) and FIAT (Field Information Agency, Technical) documents are abstracts of captured enemy documents of World War II. The abstractors are arbitrarily indexed and referenced as the authors. Thus, an article written by Schultz, translated and abstracted by Jones, appears in reference as:

1. Jones, A. B., "Olefins," *BIOS Report* No. 578 (1950).

Some of these reports are interviews of captured scientists and again the interviewer is the author. The man interviewed takes secondary precedence as:

2. Whitney, W. K., "Analysis of Phosphorus-bearing Ores," (Interrogation of J. K. Schumaker), *FIAT Report* No. 1387 (1951).

The Office of Technical Services (OTS) of the U.S. Department of Commerce handled the distribution of these reports to American users. OTS, now called Clearing House for Federal Scientific and Technical Information (CHFSTI), publisher U.S. Government Research Reports, which lists all their available printed or microfilm reports. Most of these reports listed by the OTS were given a Publication Board (PB) number which is used in references. German patents and patent applications appearing in the U.S. Government Research Reports are given PB numbers.

3. Farrington, D. C. and Clark, P. E., "Pesticides," (Interrogation of J. P. Wallace), *BIOS Final Report* No. 123 (1951), PB 10364.

Research has taken place under industrial contract with the War Production Board (WPB), which worked through the Office of Scientific Research and Development (OSRD) or through the National Defense Research Committee (NDRC). These research results were given to a governmental agency as secret, confidential, or restricted reports, and their distribution limited until declassified at the end of World War II. More and more frequently these reports are being listed in *Chemical Abstracts*.

4. Schmidt, T. L., "Microanalysis of Boron," *OSRD Report* No. 1082 (1947), available from CHFSTI.

Patents

References to patents are as important as references to journals, and equal care must be used to make certain the reader can locate the original source.

Patents should be cited in the following manner: Inventor, assignee, title, country, patent number, publication, application, and priority dates. When a patent includes both an application date and a priority date (date of application in a country other than in the country of issue), only the priority date should be given. For example:

1. Stoffel, P. J. (to Monsanto Co.), "Composition and Method for Controlling Undesirable Vegetation," **U.S. 3,066,021** (cl. 267-89.9), Jan. 24, 1963; Ger. Appl. Nov. 6, 1955; 2 pp.

A patent with only publication and application dates is written:

2. Perron, K. L. (to ABC Electronics, Inc.), "Dienes," **Fr. 1,312,535** (cl. D 01 *d*), Dec. 21, 1964, Appl. Nov. 9, 1965; 4 pp.

A patent with publication, application, and multiple priority dates in one country shows only the earliest priority date as:

3. Buehler, F. A. and Andress, H. J. (to Socony Mobil Co., Inc.), "Polysiloxane-amine Mixtures," **Belg. 616,434,** July 30, 1962; U.S. Appl. Apr. 14, 1961, 18 pp.

A patent which has an addition patent is shown as:

4. Comte, F. (to Monsanto Co.), "Polycaprolactam Powder," **Brit. 914,022** (cl. C 08 *g*), Dec. 28, 1962; U.S. Appl. Aug. 20, 1958; 7 pp. Addn. to **Brit. 872,382.**

"Division of" or "Continuation-in-part of" should replace "Addn. to" when appropriate.

In some foreign countries a company can apply for the patent, and so its name may be the only one given. For instance:

5. Standard Francaise des Petroles, "Lubricants," **Fr. 935,762,** Jan. 17, 1965 (*CA* 55, 20365c).

Note, if an abstract has been prepared, a reference to that abstract should be given.

The abstract reference should be given first if the patent itself was not used as the source of information. For example:

> 6. Winkler, J. V., *CA* **58**, 10390*h*; (to Gulf Research and Development Co.), "Oil Additives," **U.S. 2,740,725,** Apr. 5, 1965.

Chemical Abstracts uses the abbreviations: U.S., Brit., Ger., Swed., Japan., Ital., Fr., and U.S.S.R., and Swiss is written out when listing patents.

Unpublished Material

Information used in a report may come from material that has not been published, but yet is available to the writer. Papers presented at technical meetings, personal letters, and personal conversations are some of these sources. The citations should be given as exactly as possible so that the reader can judge the source of the information.

In-company reports, private communications or letters may be used as references as they are usually available to a company employee.

> 1. Young, G. M., Aluminum Co. of Canada, Ltd., Montreal, letter to R. H. Rimmer, Aluminum Lab. Ltd., Kingston, Jan. 13, 1965.

Papers presented at meetings are usually listed in printed programs. Reference can be made as follows:

> 1. Klein, S., "Automatic Decoding of Written English," Unpublished doctoral dissertation, University of California, Berkeley, 1963.
> 2. Oettinger, A. G., "Mathematical Linguistics and Automatic Translation," Report presented to the National Science Foundation, No. NSF-8, Cambridge, Mass., Jan. 1963.
> 3. Waldo, W. H., "Significant Later Advances in Handling Chemical Structural Information," Paper presented as part of the Symposium: Chemical Notation Systems—The NRC Report and Subsequent Developments, Div. Chem. Lit., Am. Chem. Soc., Chicago National Meeting, Fall, 1964.

Report on Microfilm

1. Rafferty, Nancy J., "Relationship Between the Pronephros and Haploid Syndrome in Frog Larvae," Ph.D. Thesis, Univ. of Ill. (L. C. Card No. Mic. 64-4789), 50 pp. Univ. Microfilms, Ann Arbor, Mich., Dissertation Abstr. 20, 1146 (1965).

Notebook References

Reference should be made in internal research reports to the notebooks in which the original work can be found. The references should be placed directly after the assembled bibliography. For instance:

1. Marshall, A. B., K-28 Notebook No. ML-108 (1955), pp. 25-30.
2. Mueller, W. K., "Azobenzene Materials," Dow Chem. Co., Midland, Mich., Feb. 17, 1965, Notebook No. R-BB-865-42-90.

Considerable has been said and written about the ethics of publications for science, about high honor giving credit where credit is due, about copyright protection against those who may plagiarize. Sincerity of purpose, however, can be detected by the pertinence of the selected bibliography and the accuracy of the citations.

CHAPTER 7 *Punctuation Signals the Meaning*

Technical writing is not exempt from the rules of good punctuation. The author who wishes his work to be read smoothly and accurately should give close attention to its punctuation. Punctuation marks help the reader find the exact meaning; they help to separate words and thoughts and so present them distinctly; they help to group and keep together related ideas; and to set off certain words for emphasis. Their use affects the tempo of writing. Too many punctuation marks may slow the reader to the point of exasperation, and too few may fail to convey a clear message.

A good working rule is that if a sentence has to be reread by someone reasonably familiar with the subject in order to determine the meaning, some further punctuation is probably desirable. An author should also remember that if his article is written for a journal it probably will be read by foreigners who will find adequate punctuation extremely helpful. For the most part the rules summarized in any good dictionary will answer questions on good usage.* Some technical uses of punctuations are not given in dictionaries.

C. C. Travis, Jr. writing in the October, 1964 issue of *STWP Review,* (the publication of the Society of Technical Writers and Publishers) describes in detail how to punctuate mathematical equations and suggests how to type them. There are also special

* "Webster's Seventh New Collegiate Dictionary," G. and C. Merriam Co., Springfield, Mass., 1964.

situations for punctuation in chemistry. The "Style Manual for Biological Journals" published by the American Institute of Biological Sciences suggests punctuation for complex biological reactions, biochemical equations, and metabolic quotients. For instance: Use a centered period for water of hydration in chemical formulas ($Na_2B_4O_7 \cdot 10H_2O$).

Most marks come naturally. Even in a hastily written first draft the author will feel the natural grouping of his ideas sufficiently to mark the sentences and most of the subordinate elements in some reasonable way. But punctuation is not completely automatic, even with practiced writers. The author who put at the end of a class paper "no time to punctuate" was, perhaps, wiser than he intended, for punctuation needs careful checking in revision.

Since readers have come to understand punctuation as a signal in interpreting what they read, it is to a writer's interest to know and to follow the usual conventions and also to know where he has opportunity for choice.

Open and Close Punctuation

The current trend of most editors and even more of writers, technical or professional, is toward open punctuation—the use of fewer punctuating marks. Close punctuation is the use of many marks, almost to the point of reader exasperation.

Sentence movement is the chief controlling factor. More complicated, not necessarily longer, sentences need more and heavier marks than simpler ones, for example, semicolons instead of commas to guide the reader. An author's tempo also has bearing, since punctuation marks have the effect of slowing up the reading; a swiftly moving style, especially in narrative, needs few marks. In a technical report, the introduction, discussion, and conclusions normally have faster-moving styles than the body. Thus more punctuation marks are necessary in the detailed sections of reports.

All this suggests that before an author can think intelligently about a specific mark of punctuation in his report writing he needs to know something about his general style—whether it is involved and formal, requiring the support of a number of marks, or straightforward and simple, needing few marks.

Good technical authors write directly, or soon learn to, and follow the open style, using the marks to emphasize the structure and meaning of sentences. They omit all punctuation that does not add to clearness.

I have omitted many of the common rules of punctuation, giving emphasis to the less known technical rules, the practice of the scientific fraternity, and the exceptional.

Period

(1) Use a period:

    (a) after abbreviations of Latin words *e.g., i.e., et al.* (note: no period after the Latin word *et*); titles (Mr., Dr., etc.); when an abbreviation spells a word (in., Fig., no., sol., etc.); after journal abbreviations (*Am. J. Phys.*), and words (Sept., Vol., a.m., Co.) unless the abbreviation has, through usage, become a symbol, for example, Btu, fps, emf, and esu. (See Appendix A for a list of abbreviations approved by the American Institute of Physics.)

    (b) at the end of a quote, inside the quotation marks: "Clear thinking is directly related to clear writing." Or: In recent years, writers and editors in the medical sciences have been included in the reference to "technical."

    (c) inside or outside parentheses or brackets, depending on whether the parenthetical matter is an independent sentence (the period goes inside) or is a subordinate part of the main sentence (the period goes outside).

(2) Use three spaced periods to indicate the omission of words or ellipsis from a quoted passage, thus: "Ultimate success ... depends on future development." If the omitted words conclude a sentence, place the ellipsis before the period.... If the omitted words are the first part of a second sentence in the quotation, place the ellipsis after the period.... (Notice the difference in spacing

after the word *period* in the two preceding sentences.) If a paragraph is omitted in a quotation, use a whole line of periods; however, some journals use three asterisks.

(3) Omit the period after:

    (a) chemical symbols (Fe, Ca, O); abbreviation of mathematical symbols (sin, tan, log); organizations known by initials (YMCA, CBS, AFL-CIO); government commissions (AEC, NSF, DDC, USDA); biochemical compounds (Leu, ACTH, RNA); societies (IRE, STWP); international agencies (ICC, UNESCO).

    (b) contractions for units of measurement, such as 2 mg/ml, μc, wt, cm, because the current trend among technical journals is to avoid a period after the abbreviation of a word or contraction of a unit of measure unless required for clarity.

    (c) Roman numerals and ordinal numbers (VIII, 24th).

    (d) legends for tables, titles, subtitles, headings, and subheadings, except run-in subheadings where a period, semicolon, or dash is necessary.

(4) There is frequently much ado among editors and typists about the position of superscripts, parentheses, quotation marks, and other minor punctuation marks in front of, or following the period at the end of a sentence. Unless there are specific rules to the contrary set forth by journals or in company style manuals, the following logic should hold for these minor, but emotion-laden details.

The minor mark follows the period when it refers to the entire sentence as a unit, but if the minor mark refers to any fragment of the sentence less than the entire sentence, then it should appear before the period. For example, if a sentence is being quoted or if reference is being made to it, the quotation mark, or superscript reference number will appear following the period; whereas if less than a sentence is being quoted or if the reference is to a man's name or a document that appears in the sentence then, of course, the quotation mark or reference number should appear before the period.

Centered or Raised Period

(1) Use a raised period for:
  (a) water of hydration or other biomolecular salt complexes in chemical formulas ($ZnNH_4PO_4 \cdot H_2O$).
  (b) chemical bonds if the standard dash occupies too much space.
  (c) genetic expressions, such as: $AA \cdot AB \cdot AC \cdot BB \cdot BC \cdot CC$.
  (d) multiplication when equations are too crowded to permit use of the times ($\times$) sign or when use of closed-up or thinly spaced symbols is not satisfactory, for instance: $T \times c \times (x + Y)$ may be printed $Tc(x + Y)$, or $T \cdot c(x + Y)$.

Comma

About half the total number of punctuation marks used in writing are commas and probably the question, "Should a comma be here?" is the most usual one asked in revising a report. It is hard to answer, because the comma is a light mark without any special tone or meaning of its own, as the colon and dash so conspicuously have, and yet it is tremendously useful in clarifying meaning.

Fundamentally a comma is a mark of slight separation. The separation is ever so slight in the conventional uses (as in dates, words in series), but in most instances it is just sufficient to keep words or phrases distinct and so make them more easily understood, and give a slight emphasis to what follows. The rules below are not complete, but represent guides for the commonly asked questions.

(1) Use a comma:
  (a) between two independent clauses joined by a coordinating conjunction (*and, but, for, or, not, yet, so, also, neither, therefore*). If the clauses contain internal punctuation, separate them with a semicolon.

Communication is to pass an idea from one mind to another, but it does not mean to pass words from one mind to another.

(b) to set off a dependent introductory clause begun with a subordinating conjunction (*if, although, since, when, where, because*). If the preceding phrase contains an infinitive, a participle, or a gerund, it is generally set off by a comma to prevent misreading, such as:

When the drilling began, knocking the bottles off the shelf, all the employees left.

(c) to separate words in apposition, geographical names, items in dates and addresses.

Dwight E. Gray, Science Liaison Officer of the OSI at the NSF, has written many papers in the areas of science information.
On Tuesday, December 31, 1964, he arrived in Washington, D.C.

(d) to separate clauses, words, or phrases, and coordinate adjectives modifying the same noun.

Benzene, toluene, and xylene are useful as solvents. A. B. Jones, C. B. Smith, and T. L. Brown wrote a paper on succinic, fumaric, malic, and oxaloacetic acids.

(e) to separate conjunctive adverbs (*therefore, thus, then, still, however, accordingly, moreover, nevertheless, consequently*) and transitional phrases [*on the contrary* (*but* might be a better choice), *on the other hand, in fact, after all, in the first place* (*first* is better)].

(f) to set off a short quotation. Use a colon if the quotation is long.

(g) to set off inserted phrases, such as: "A marked difference in structure, as shown in Fig. 1, took place in the heparin suspension."

(h) for contrast of words or phrases. "You have..., not ...,"; "Neither..., nor...."

(i) to separate phrases and clauses placed out of the more common positions for emphasis.

The director, says the group leader, needs a new office. (Notice the difference in meaning when the commas are omitted.)

(j) to separate adjacent sets of figures.

By 1968, 300 compounds . . . .

(k) to separate superscript or subscript.

See Roe[3,5,7] for a description of $C_{5,6,7}$ aromatic rings.

(2) Omit the comma:
   (a) if two independent clauses joined by a coordinating conjunction are short and no ambiguity results.

The reaction boiled and the solid disappeared.

   (b) after a short introductory phrase begun with a preposition, if no ambiguity results.

On Thursday the new labs were begun.

   (c) after equation and formulas set off from the text by centering on the page.

$$\log_e 2 = \eta t = 0.693$$

   (d) around short appositives.

The kinetic energy Q is . . . .
The enzyme pepsin is a protein.

Semicolon

The semicolon is used to separate sentence parts of equal rank such as main clauses not joined by a coordinating conjunction, and phrases or clauses containing commas, even when joined by coordinating conjunctions.

(1) Use the semicolon to separate:
   (a) coordinate clauses not joined by a conjunction.

The radioactive isotope of an element behaves chemically exactly like the normal atoms of that element; it differs only that on its disruption its presence is revealed.

(b) coordinate elements containing internal punctuation.

On exposure to deuterons for a few seconds the most inferior amber-tinted diamond takes a permanent green tint equal to that of the best natural gems; however, on heating to a very high temperature the amber tint may be restored.

(c) elements of a series if the elements contain internal punctuation.

Chemical blood analyses are helpful in clinical diagnosis; hypergly-cemia, or other abnormality, in diabetes; low phosphorus, ascorbic acid, and increased phosphatase in rickets.

(2) Place the semicolon *outside* the quotation mark.

Colon

Colon and semicolon, notwithstanding the similarity of the names, differ widely in use. The semicolon is a strong separator, almost equal to a period, and is used only between equal parts. The colon is an introducer, pointing to something that is to follow.

(1) Use a colon:
  (a) to introduce a long quotation. A comma is sufficient for short ones.
  (b) to introduce a list or enumeration.
  (c) to emphasize a sequence in thought between two complete sentences when the emphasis obtained by a period or word, such as *namely,* is insufficient.

There is one chance for complete vaporization: one source of constant temperature and constant pressure.

  (d) to separate a complete clause from a following illustrative clause or phrase.

The most rapid method requires determining an efficient program to use: First, calculate the number of cards to go into the computer.

The colon may be followed by either a small letter or a capital.

(e) to separate parts of ratios. The slant line, solidus, or virgule, also can be used if there are only two elements in the ratio, but in a three-element ratio do not use the slant line.

(f) to direct attention in a business letter following the salutation, to the title of a book or paper following the name of the author, or to the minute following the hour.

Dear Sir:
Colin Cherry: *On Human Communication* (*A Review, a Survey, and a Criticism*).
8:30 a.m.

Slant Line (Solidus or Virgule)

(1) The slant line (/) is a mathematical mark of division (¾).

(2) It can be used instead of a colon to indicate ratio (A/G or A:G), but not if the ratio involves more than two elements. For instance, 3:5:7 is clear, but 3/5/7 is not.

(3) The slant line should not be used as shorthand for *per* if more than one is required.

"1,000 drops per square foot per week," should not be written "1,000 drops/ft²/wk"; instead the author should write "1,000 drops/ sq ft wk," or "1,000 drops/(sq ft × wk)," so that both square foot and week fall in the denominator where they belong.

(4) Avoid expressions such as: and/or and time/rest ratio. For instance:

The animals were subjected to rest and/or activity. This can be expressed: The animals were subjected to rest, or activity, or both. There are two uses for *or* recognized by logicians: The inclusive *or* and the restrictive *or*. Authors are obliged to indicate the meaning clearly and not leave it in doubt.

Apostrophe

The apostrophe is normally used (1) to indicate the possessive case of nouns and indefinite pronouns, but not of personal pronouns; (2) to mark omissions in contracted words or numerals; and (3) to form the plural of letters, figures, or symbols. The simple system of "Webster" * is recommended for teachnical authors because it is established in all writing, and it requires no consideration of the pronunciation of a foreign name (such as the silent *s* in Dumas).

> Adams', Baeyer's, Berzelius', Darzens', Charles's, James's.

However, the following alternative expressions are correct and perhaps better:

> Adams catalyst, by the Darzens reaction, with Ringers solution, Charles law.

Pedestrian traffic at intersections is usually regulated by signs that read: DONT WALK. There have been those who criticise this omission of the apostrophe as slovenly, even though we live in a world which seems to be eager to rid itself of the past.

The interesting fact is that the apostrophe is a printer's problem and has little to do with the language itself. About 1680 it was first used to indicate a genitive singular and about a hundred years later to indicate a genitive plural. But it is now in the process of really disappearing, no matter what grammarians cry about the "lamp of learning flickering out."

The Board of Geographic Names has dropped apostrophes from place names, such as Hells Canyon or Eagles Pass, not Hell's Canyon or Eagle's Pass.

Quotation Marks

(1) Use double quotation marks in the text around:
   (a) all direct quotations.
   (b) titles of articles, parts of books, and series titles.

---

* Here and elsewhere for simplicity the name "Webster" is used to denote the Merriam-Webster Collegiate Dictionary.

(c) new technical terms or old terms used in a new or unusual sense.

(2) Use single quotation marks around a word, title, term, or quotation within a quotation.

> "We replied to your question, 'Where do mutations occur?' and you wondered at our answer, 'Chromosomes.'"

(3) If a quotation extends over more than one paragraph, begin each paragraph with quotation marks, but close the quotation only at the end of the last paragraph.

(4) Place a comma or period *inside* the closing quotation mark, even if it is not part of the quotation. Place the colon and semicolon *outside* the quotation marks. Place question marks and dashes *inside* the quotation when they belong to the quotation, *outside* if they do not.

When quotation marks are not used around quotations it is customary to indent and single-space the quote. For example, note the way the classic quote from Elmer W. Shaw, first published in *Science*, **121,** 567(1955), appears here:

Ten Commandments for Technical Writers

(1) Thou shalt remember thy readers all the days of thy life; for without readers thy words are as naught.

(2) Thou shalt not forsake the time-honored virtue of simplicity.

(3) Thou shalt not abuse the third person passive.

(4) Thou shalt not dangle thy participles; neither shalt thou misplace thy modifiers.

(5) Thou shalt not commit monotony.

(6) Thou shalt not cloud thy message with a miasma of technical jargon.

(7) Thou shalt not hide the fruits of thy research beneath excess verbiage; neither shalt thou obscure thy conclusions with vague generalities.

(8) Thou shalt not resent helpful advice from thy editors, reviewers, and critics.

(9) Thou shalt consider also the views of the layman, for his is an insight often unknown to technocrats.

(10) Thou shalt write and rewrite without tiring, for such is the key to improvement.

Question Mark

(1) Use a question mark:

(a) at the end of a direct question, even if the question is presented in declarative form.

Will you write again if I can be of further service?

However, many writers feel it is courteous to follow such declarative sentences in business letters by a period.

(b) to express (within parentheses) the writer's uncertainty as to the correctness of the preceding word or fact.

Alaric was born in 376 (?) and died in 410.

(2) Do not use a question mark after an indirect question.

Exclamation Point

The exclamation point is rarely used in scientific writing. Its use to mean factorial in mathematics seems to be the major technical use.

$$Y = 2!$$

Dash

The dash is twice as long as the hyphen and used to set off a parenthetical element; to indicate an afterthought or an abrupt change in construction; or to summarize a list of items. It should be used sparingly.

Parentheses, dashes, commas—all are used to set off parenthetical matter.

(1) Use a dash

(a) between superscript or subscript letters or figures to indicate inclusiveness.

See Smythe [5-9] for a summary of C_{3-8} aromatic rings.

(b) to indicate an abrupt break or shift in thought.

(c) to separate parenthetical matter, especially to secure emphasis.

The chief part—more than 70%—was carbon.

(d) to indicate that an important thought is coming next.

Hyphen

A hyphen is used when a word is broken at the end of a line. Divide words between syllables only, consulting a dictionary for the proper syllabification.

No simple rule governs the punctuation of two words customarily used as a unit. The trend in technical writing is away from hyphenated words (end-point) and toward either separate (end point) or typographically solid words (endpoint).

For nonscientific words "Webster's Seventh New Collegiate Dictionary" is an unquestionable authority. W. J. Gensler and K. D. Gensler have written one of the most complete books on specialized technical writing, "Writing Guide for Chemists," (McGraw-Hill Book Co., Inc., New York, 1961) in which they discuss associated word pairs and hyphenation in detail. The "U.S. Government Printing Office Style Manual," (revised ed., Superintendent of Documents, Washington 25, D.C., 1959) gives many rules on compounding words as well as fifty pages of examples.

Generally words with prefixes such as anti-, semi-, re-, non-, pseudo-, quasi-, and un- are written without the hyphen unless the meaning is changed when written as one word (un-ionized, not unionized).

When two words standing just before a noun jointly modify that noun, a hyphen between the two words may speed reading comprehension.

    water-soluble compound
    hydrogen-ion concentration
    10-ml flask
    high-melting solid

Hyphenation is incorrect when the first word of a two-word modifier is an adverb ending in *ly*. For example:

completely oxidized material
carefully filled cylinder
fully packed column

Two-word names of compounds remain unhyphenated when used as modifiers before a noun.

sodium hydroxide solution

(1) Use a hyphen:
    (a) between the numerator and denominator of a fraction when spelled out (one-fourth).
    (b) between numbers to indicate a range (56-75). This implies inclusiveness.
    (c) compound words used as single modifying adjectives.

d-c motor, well-known make, *o-*, *p-*, *m*-toluene

    (d) when numbers come together as part of an adjectival grouping before a noun.

two 25-cc pipets, four three-necked flasks

    (e) between spelled-out numbers: twenty-one through twenty-nine, thirty-one through thirty-nine, etc.; these are always hyphenated.
    (f) when the word for which an abbreviation stands is hyphenated; the abbreviation should be hyphenated, such as:

ft-lb for foot-pound.

When *like* is a suffix, no hyphen is used, unless the main word is long or ends in *l*, tarlike, armlike, ball-like, gel-like.

No hyphen is used when a spelled-out number is combined with the suffix *fold* as in fivefold. But when a figure is followed by *fold* a hyphen is used, as in 5-fold.

Hyphens may be inserted to indicate omission in a series when the same omission is common to every item but the last. But do not use hyphens unless they are helpful. For example:

> Volumes were checked at 2, 4, and 6-hour runs. (*2-, 4-,* and *6-hour* offers little advantage.)
> Dimethyl-, trimethyl-, and methylethylacetic acid were prepared. (Here the hyphens stress the incomplete names.)

"Hawley's Technical Speller," by G. G. Hawley and A. W. Hawley, (Reinhold Pub. Corp., New York, 1955) is a classic and an excellent source for the use of hyphens in chemical terminology. For a list of the more common technical hyphenated and nonhyphenated words see Appendix C.

Parentheses

Parentheses set off parts loosely joined to the sentence and tend to obscure the parts thus set off. Parentheses should be used sparingly except for several special cases.

(1) Use parentheses:

    (a) to set off comment or explanation that is structurally independent of the sentence.

> Crude material is mixed in vapor form with air (1 to 35) by spraying.

    (b) to group mathematical expressions.

$$W = 3.0(V_2 - V_1)$$

    (c) to label enumerations included within a paragraph.

> The three reactions were (1), (2), and (3).

    (d) to set off segments in chemical nomenclature.

> N-(2-chloroallyl)acetamide

(2) Use single parentheses to set off enumerated paragraphs.

    1), A), x)

(3) Avoid the use of double parentheses, but when used make certain there are the same number of right parentheses as left.

poly(adenylyl-(3′ → 5′)-guanosine 3′-phosphate)

(4) When a sentence demands other marks of punctuation with parenthetical matter, these marks are placed after the second parenthesis. If a phrase at the end of a sentence is enclosed in parentheses, the closing parenthesis is placed inside the period.

Brackets

(1) Use brackets:
    (a) around parenthetical remarks inserted within other parenthetical remarks. And these can be enclosed by braces. These are called signs of aggregation.

$$R_a = \{30 \div [(459 + 32) \times 0.081]\} = 0.754$$

    (b) to set off correction or interpolations made in a quotation by the person using the quotation.

Mechanics is based upon three principles [Newton's laws of motion].
The first plant [1964] was built entirely of molded plastic.
Gypsum and barites are grouped as sulfates [*sic*]. (A bracketed *sic* tells the reader that the error appears in the original—it is not merely a misprint.)

The special use of punctuation marks in technical literature has evolved gradually in each discipline rather independently. The editors of the high-prestige journals in each of the scientific disciplines have faced and solved many of their own specialized forms. Although there is no right nor wrong about these uses, there are acceptable and unacceptable forms based, largely, on the practice of these journals. An author writing for a journal for the first time should study the journal characteristics carefully. The same advice goes for reports in differing companies and institutions. Be an innovator with the greatest of care.

CHAPTER 8

Technical English

Communication through equations, chemical or mathematical, is highly concise; it has little of the redundancy of English. As a result, great care must be exercised to assure accuracy and completeness. Proofreading and definition of terms are much more important for documents containing many equations.

On the other hand, communication by equation has the advantage of explicitness, often unattainable in English or other natural language. It is frequently more elegant, and because of its conciseness, conveys much more information per character or page than natural language. These "scientific" languages have conventions and "grammars" all their own.

Specialized terms or "jargon" and abbreviations are often used as a substitute for equations. Although such techniques are not nearly so elegant as equations, their use does serve to improve conciseness often at the expense of clarity. Their widespread use, therefore, requires careful adherence to conventions to maintain a clear expression of meaning.

Equations

Many technical reports contain long, involved equations that are difficult to prepare neatly. Numbers, letters, and symbols in formulas and equations must be clear and accurate, and in proper alignment. Authors should allow extra space—triple or even quadruple—around typewritten equations. If an author's typewriter does not have special symbols, he can draw them neatly by hand.

It is not considered good form to begin a sentence with a mathematical symbol or with a number, particularly when the preceding sentence ends in a number or symbol. If it is necessary to begin a sentence with a number, the author should write out the number. He should not use a numeral. All symbols used in equations must be defined.

There are several good manuals and books that describe in detail how to write equations and symbols so that they can easily be read or set in type.

(1) American Institute of Physics, "Style Manual," revised 2nd ed., 335 East 45th Street, New York 17, New York, 1964, p. 15.

(2) Chemical Abstracts Service, "Directions for Abstractors," Am. Chem. Soc., Ohio State Univ., Columbus, Ohio, 1964, p. 3-6.

(3) Conference of Biological Editors, "Style Manual for Biological Journals," Am. Inst. Biol. Sci., 2000 P Street, NW, Washington 6, D.C., 1961, p. 43.

(4) Gensler, W. J. and Gensler, K. D., "Writing Guide for Chemists," McGraw-Hill Book Co., Inc., New York, 1961.

(5) Travis, C. C., Jr., "Aids for the Typist Mean Better, Faster Equation Composition," *STWP Review*, 11(4), 9 (1964).

If possible the author should write equations on only one line and keep the relation of the various quantities clear.

For example, the expression $z = \dfrac{a+b}{c}$ should be written $z = (a + b)/c$ rather than $z = a + b/c$. And $c = x + y/z$ should be written $c = x + (y/z)$ to avoid any misunderstanding.

Related equations should be numbered consecutively for convenient reference in the text when discussing the equations. For instance,

$$NaOH + NaHCO_3 \rightarrow Na_2CO_3 + H_2O \tag{1}$$

$$12\,NaF + Al_2O_3 + 6\,NaHCO_3 \rightarrow 2\,Na_3AlF_6 + 6\,Na_2CO_3 + 3\,H_2O \tag{2}$$

The author ought to avoid using a chemical symbol that can be mistaken for a word, particularly in beginning a sentence, such as: *He* was found in the mixture, or *As* in these compounds indicate they might be tried as insecticides.

The formulas of simple organic substances may be used in the text if they save space, and if they can be printed in a single line, such as CH_3COOH. An author should avoid ambiguous formulas like $C_4H_4O_2$, which might mean any of eight compounds.

In naming unusual inorganic or organic compounds the conventions established by *Chemical Abstracts Service* should always be followed. For a nominal price the latest definitive nomenclature rules of IUPAC (International Union of Pure and Applied Chemistry) can be obtained from this source, and they also appear in *The Journal of the American Chemical Society* at various times, such as, *J. Am. Chem. Soc.* **82**, 5523-84(1960).

Tetravalent uranium should be written *uranium (IV)*, and trivalent iron as *iron (III)*.

Where structures of organic substances are important, type or draw them carefully centered between lines of text.

Isotopically labeled elements are indicated in American journals by the atomic weight of the isotope placed as a superior figure to the right of the symbol ($CH_3C^{14}OOH$ for acetic acid-1-C^{14}, $C^{14}H_3COOH$ for acetic acid-2-C^{14}). British journals place the atomic weight to the left.

When the name rather than the formula is used, the author should place the symbol of the isotope after the name, as in thymidine-H_3. If the position of the labeled element is known, the author should show this by a number before the symbol, such as sodium propionate-2-C^{14}; if it is unknown, or if the labeling is general, omit the number as in glucose-C^{14}.

If compounds are discussed by name in the text and if there are equations showing how these compounds are made or showing mechanism of a reaction, the names of all but the common compounds should be typed out under their formulas in the equations.

CO[OH $CONH_2COOH$

$+ H]NHCH_2COOH \rightarrow$

Hippuric acid

Analytical Results

Report analytical results in the conventional manner:

Anal.: $C_{17}H_{20}N_4O_4$; calcd: C, 59.29; H, 5.85; N, 16.27
found: C, 58.8; H, 6.03; N, 16.2

Note the punctuation, the omission of the percentage symbol, and that the calculated values may be given to four significant figures. The analytical results are given to only three figures, the last being adjusted. The fourth figure is not justified unless the most extreme precautions are taken.

The author should report the data on physical properties in the text in the standard form, indicating special conditions of measurement:

Boiling point: bp 140°C at 16 mm
Melting point: 150-152°C (unc) or (cor), (copper block), (sealed tube)
Specific refractive index: $[n]_D^{16} = 1.5892$
Specific rotation: $[\alpha]_D^{22} = \pm 2°$ (1.0 M in water)

Record temperature, wavelength of the light used in measuring specific rotation, the solvent, and concentration of the solute. Always designate R_f values with solvent and standard used. (Note both letters are italicized.)

An author should void the ambiguous term "mixed melting point" by writing:

mp 164-167°C (unc), and the mixture with an authentic sample of mp 165-166°C (unc) had mp 163-166°C (unc).

Boiling points are recorded at atmospheric pressure unless otherwise stated.

Numbers

Some writers tend to spell out numbers in the text of technical writing, but number-words can often be so long as to be unwieldy. A convenient, though arbitrary, rule is to use figures for any number requiring more than one compound word or more than two separate words. According to these limits, the following may be given as words: thirty-six, three-fifths, three hundred, one million, but 475 and 3.55 are written as figures. Another rule: For abstract numbers and enumerations in technical reports, words are preferred for numbers under 10. Be consistent, use one or the other rule. A sentence should not begin with figures. Either the corresponding word can be used, or the sentence can be recast. For example:

6 ml of acetic acid was used for recrystallization.

This should be changed to:

Six ml of acetic acid was used for recrystallization.

Or, better changed to:

Recrystallization required 6 ml of acetic acid.

When necessary to follow one number with another, separate them with a comma, as in dates: July 7, 1965

Numerical adjectives, ordinals, indefinite numbers, and round numbers should be written out.

Monsanto made over three million pounds of aspirin this year.
This is a third of the total sample.
Millions of insects will be destroyed because of radiation.

In an expression of a series of numbers in which strict adherence to a rule of style will cause part of the numbers to be in numerals and part in words, use numerals throughout.

There were 3, 8, 13, and 1,280 cells per ml of serum.

Numbers given in range, such as inclusive page numbers, should be repeated in full in the second number in the text.

The chapter ran from page 218 to 294. (not 218-94)
98.0-98.6 (not 98.0-8.6)
231-239 ml (not 231-9 ml)

The operation of extracting the root of a number may be indicated by a fractional superscript rather than by the author drawing a radical sign, *i.e.*, $20^{4/3}$ instead of $\sqrt[3]{20^4}$, or $(2\pi r)^{2/3}$ instead of $\sqrt[3]{(2\pi r)^2}$.

When a modifier and a compound modifier call for two numbers in succession, avoid writing both numbers as figures. Write 4 two-gram weights or four 2-g wts, but not 2 4-g weights.

In decimal fractions a zero should appear before the decimal point; that is, write 0.0036, not .0036.

Decimal forms should not be written with zeros to the right of the last significant figure greater than zero unless the accuracy indicated exists. The significant places should reflect the accuracy of measurement. The meanings of 1.0 g and 1.00 g are not the same. The number 5,200,024 as an experimentally determined quantity implies that the measurement is significant to seven places. A more appropriate number might be 5.2×10^6, which indicates a more modest—and probably a more realistic—two-place significance.

The number of significant places before and after arithmetical manipulation should correspond. For instance: A weight of 10.5 g might be translated to 0.00892 mole, but not to 0.0089234 mole. A yield of 56 g might correspond to a yield of 74%, but not to a yield of 74.35%.

In figures ten thousand or greater, a comma inserted every three places to the left of the decimal point is a help to the reader.

4028; 10,000; 27,546; 45,500,100

Some writers prefer a comma even in four-place numbers, as in 2,364.

In all cases where abbreviations are used following the numerical quantity, numbers should be used.

1 ml, 33 gal, 10 cm; not 24 milliliters or thirty-five ml.

Dates, page numbers, figure numbers, column numbers, run numbers, sample numbers, addresses, exact times of the day, and decimals should be given in figures.

Do not show the dollar sign ($) with a number or amount in one part of the text and the cent sign (¢) with a number or amount in another place. Use one or the other consistently.

If the dollar sign is used in expressing money values, the places indicating cents should always be filled in, even though the sum may be an even number of dollars ($5,000.00).

The significance of 42 ± 2 is uncertain because ± 2 can have several meanings. To avoid ambiguity, the nature of the precision measure should be stated explicitly—as standard deviation, extreme range, mean deviation, or the like.

In general, a significant figure is any digit of a number which is used to help denote the size of the number other than those used to locate the decimal point. The significance of a figure depends upon the accuracy of measurement of a quantity and the computations made on the measurement. Usually, a computed value will have no more significant digits than the original measurement.

> The tensile strength is 34,505 psi. (accuracy is ± 1 psi.)
> The tensile strength is 34×10^3 psi. (accuracy is $\pm 1,000$ psi.)

For a more authoritative interpretation of the determination of significance and significant figures I can suggest the book: "Statistical Manual for Chemists" by E. L. Bauer, Academic Press, New York, 1960.

Statistics

Statistics may be used in designing an experiment; they may report a series of observations; and sometimes they are used in analyzing and interpreting quantitative data from an investigation which has been completed. Statistical methods are based on probability; thus they neither support poorly designed and insufficiently controlled experiments, nor prove the results beyond a doubt.

An author should keep in mind the normal variations in samples, reliability of analytical methods, and errors resulting from the observer. An author can calculate how to extract the most information when time or material is limited, or, if no limiting factors are known, with the least experimentation. However, statistics should not be used as a substitute for thought and good sense.

When analyzing his data, the author should emphasize his results, not the statistical methods. Unnecessary mathematical details are not the most stimulating sort of reading. If absolutely necessary they should be put in an appendix. When reporting a difference between the means (or other statistics) of two groups of results the author should show the significance or give the confidence limits. Omit long descriptions of statistical methods except in reports dealing specifically with statistics. Always cite the source of any unusual methods. Always think of the reader.

For a broader discussion on statistics the "Style Manual for Biological Journals," published by the Am. Inst. Biol. Sci., Washington, D.C., 1961, p. 45 is good. Every report writer ought to read: Huff, D., "How to Lie with Statistics," W. W. Norton, New York, 1954. He says:

"Averages and relationships and trends and graphs are not always what they seem. There may be more in them than meets the eye, and there may be a good deal less.

"The secret language of statistics, so appealing in a fact-minded culture, is employed to sensationalize, inflate, confuse, and oversimplify. Statistical methods and statistical terms are necessary in reporting the mass data of social and economic trends, business conditions, 'opinion' polls, the census. But without writers who use the words with honesty and understanding and readers who know what they mean, the result can only be semantic nonsense.

"In popular writing on scientific matters the abused statistic is almost crowding out the picture of the white-jacketed hero laboring overtime without time-and-a-half in an ill-lit laboratory. Like the 'little dash of powder, little pot of paint,' statistics are making many an important fact 'look like what she aint.' "

Darrell Huff explains his book this way: "This book is a sort of primer in ways to use statistics to deceive. It may seem altogether too much like a manual for swindlers. Perhaps I can justify it in the manner of the retired burglar whose published reminiscences amounted to a graduate course in how to pick a lock and muffle a footfall: The crooks already know these tricks; honest men must learn them in self-defense."

Italics

On the printed page, emphasis may be supplied by boldface and small capitals, as well as by italics. On the typed or handwritten page, emphasis is supplied by the underline and—not often—by double underline. When the typed or handwritten page is submitted for printer's copy, underlined material will appear in print in *italics,* and doubly underlined material will appear in SMALL CAPITALS. A wavy line under a word or number in the typed copy is the printer's mark for **boldface.**

Too many emphasis marks weaken the force of all; they should be used sparingly. Usually emphasis should be inherent in the rhetoric—the way in which the words are used, not how they are set in type.

Titles of separate publications—such as technical journals, bulletins, magazines, newspapers—are put in italics when mentioned in text. Names of ships and titles of works of art are put in italics, as are words, letters, or figures spoken of as such:

The report contains more *I*'s than *they*'s.
The number *5* is here.

Letters in mathematical formulas, except Greek letters, are italicized. Other letters that should be italicized are:

1. Letters in crystal structure space group designation:

$$D_2^4\text{-}P\,2_12_12_1$$

2. *N* for normality
3. *M* for molarity
4. *m* for molality
5. *o-, m-, p-, d-, l-, dl-, sym-, sec-, tert-,* and *meso-* to designate position or stereoisomerism in organic compounds (not abbreviated or italicized unless part of a specific compound name)
6. *R_f* in chromatography

A naturalized foreign word is not italicized. Only arbitrary decision seems to be used for determining whether a word has become familiar enough to appear without italics. "Webster" is more conservative than the technical literature, which tends to drop italics.

These Latin terms and their abbreviations do not need to be italicized in technical reports:

Word	Abbreviation	Definition
a posteriori		known through experience or facts
a priori		presumptive; deduced from self-evident principles
circa	ca.	approximately, about
compare	cf.	compare, take note of the following
exempli gratia	e.g.	for example, for instance
et alii	et al.	and others
ibidem	ibid.	in the same place
id est	i.e.	that is
in vacuo		in a vacuum
inter alia		among other things
per se		by itself, of itself, intrinsically
per os		by mouth
sic		thus (sometimes inserted in brackets to denote exact reproduction of the original)
versus	vs (no period)	in contrast to, as against
videlicet	viz.	namely

Foreign words are put in italics, such as:

ancien régime   *dolce far niente*
noblesse oblige   *rapprochement*

Italicize Latin scientific names of genera, species, subspecies, and varieties (but not groups of higher rank, as phyla, classes, orders) in botanical and zoological names.

Apomictic triploid *Rubus canadensis* L. was crossed with tetraploid blackberries.

Capitals

"Webster" is not up to date with respect to trade names or officially designated trade marks. The status of these names changes almost from week to week. When the rights are relinquished by the manufacturers of these materials, the names enter the public domain, and no longer need to be capitalized.

nylon, cellophane, saran, penicillin, monel alloy, neoprene, mercurochrome, dry ice, tygon

If there is any doubt whether to capitalize or not capitalize a trade name, conservatism is recommended; the capitalized word is always correct.

"Drierite," "Acrilan," "Frigidaire," "Aureomycin"

Registered trade marks are capitalized, and are sometimes inclosed in quotation marks to ward off complaints from the legal departments of the owners. Trade marks are often identified by placing the symbol ® after the name, or by an asterisk and accompanying footnote that might say "Registered trade mark of A-1 Corp."

In technical reports directed to a known audience the use of familiar trade names is fine, but such names should not appear alone in formal reports or manuscripts for journal publication. A satisfactory solution is to use both trade name and a supplementary description. For example:

Decolorizing carbon ("Norite") is packed in the filter.

For information on up-to-date trade names the following four books cover the field:

1. "The Merck Index," 7th ed., Merck and Co., Inc., Rahway, N.J., 1960.
2. Evers, N. and Caldwell, D., "The Chemistry of Drugs," John Wiley & Sons, Interscience, New York, 1959.
3. Zimmerman, O. T. and Lavine, I., "Handbook of Material Trade Names," supplement 3 to 1953 ed., Industrial Research Service, Inc., Dover, N.H., 1960.
4. "Thomas' Register of American Manufacturers," 54th ed., Thomas Pub. Co., New York, 1964, Vol. IV.
5. "Condensed Chemical Dictionary," 6th ed., Reinhold Pub. Corp., 1961.

Adjectives and derivatives of proper names are capitalized except when their usage has become so general that the name has been reduced to a common noun.

Capitalized	Not Capitalized
Baumé	ampere
Buchner funnel	angstrom
Claisen flask	babbitt metal
Celsius	bessemer convertor
Crookes tube	bunsen burner
Curie point	centigrade
Dewar flask	coulomb

Capitalized	Not Capitalized
Fahrenheit	curie
Glauber salt	debye
Hamiltonian	diesel motor
Jones plug	erlenmeyer flask
Jones reductor	faraday
Kelvin	fullers earth
Laplacian	gauss
Nicol prism	joule
Parr bomb	lambert
Ringers solution	ohm
Reynolds number	paris green
Vigreux column	petrie dish
	portland cement
	roentgen ray
	venturi tube
	volt

Again, if there is doubt, the capitalized word is always correct.

The nouns modified by the possessive form of proper names are not capitalized, but the names are:

Boyle's law   Einstein's theory of relativity

Names of chemicals are not capitalized, but the symbols are:

oxygen, O_2 deoxyribonucleic acid, DNA

The author can make his own decision whether to capitalize or not a.m., p.m., no., but he should be consistent throughout his report.

Capitalize the names of planets, constellations, asteroids, stars, and groups of stars, but not sun, earth, and moon unless these are listed with other astronomical names.

When first letters of principal words are being capitalized, the second part of a hyphenated word should be capitalized if it is a noun; otherwise, it should begin with a small letter.

The Reactions of Perfluoro-Olefins

In the body of the report capitalize the nouns *Chapter, Article, Experiment, Drawing,* and other often-used designations only when followed by a number or letter; when followed by page, column, and line they should be in lower case.

Abbreviations

The purpose of abbreviations is to save space and the time required in writing and in reading. When the confusion resulting from excessive use of abbreviations requires the reader to spend more time in finding the meaning of a report than in reading it, abbreviations have lost their usefulness. One of the fundamentals of clarity in reading is the physical appearance of text; therefore most abbreviations should be avoided in strictly textual material. However, abbreviations such as *Fig.* for *Figure* may be used in the text.

In tables, illustrations, and equations where arrangement and appearance have meaning, abbreviations may be used more frequently. In addition to those most common technical abbreviations listed in Appendix A (used with permission from the American Institute of Physics "Style Manual") standard abbreviations such as those in "Webster's Seventh New Collegiate Dictionary," American Standards Association's "Abbreviations for Scientific and Engineering Terms" (70 East 45th Street, New York 17, Bulletin Y1, Z10.1941), or other standard technical reference works may be used when the writer is certain that the reader will understand. The writer should not use an abbreviation unless there is a definite reason for doing so. When in doubt, spell out.

There is still no universally accepted form of abbreviations among the sciences. The American Standards Association has had wide acceptance of its list, which has promoted the trend to drop periods from technical abbreviations—as in *amt, wt, cm, bp,* and *mg* (however, *in.* for inch, to avoid confusion with the word *in*). The widely accepted list of abbreviations of the American Institute of Physics drops the periods on abbreviations, as does the bulletin for chemical engineers, "Letter Symbols for Chemical Engineering" (ASA Y10.12-1955). The biological journals favor dropping periods after abbreviations as suggested in "Style Manual for Biological Journals" prepared by the Committee on Form and Style of the Conference of Biological Editors, 1960. The *Journal of the American Medical Association* drops the periods from their abbreviated journal references.

However, the journals published by the American Chemical Society retain periods in abbreviations. For their list of abbreviations and symbols see the 1964 "Directions for Abstractors."

Recommendations of the IUPAC on units and physical and chemical quantities are available from Chemical Abstracts Service or may be found in *J. Am. Chem. Soc.* **82,** 5517(1960).

The British opinion on abbreviation is given in a report by the Symbols Committee of the Royal Society called "Symbols, Signs, and Abbreviations," (*J. Chem. Soc.* **1951,** 1677).

The recommendations of a committee of physicists on English and Greek letter symbols is found in the section on common abbreviations and symbols in the "Handbook of Chemistry and Physics." *

A technical author should consult one or more of these lists and decide on a set of abbreviations and symbols and use them consistently in his writing. Generally the policy of editors or research directors will determine the practice he must follow.

Abbreviations of units and for percent (%) should be used only with exact figures, and approximations with numbers, but not with no figures at all.

Tensile strength equals 24,000 psi.
Tensile strength is near 15,000 psi.
Tensile strength is measured in pounds per square inch.

Abbreviations of units are written in the same way for the singular and the plural. However, the terms *Figs. 1* and *2, Vols. 3* to *5,* and *Nos. 27* through *30* are exceptions to this rule.

The # sign is *never* used in technical reports to stand for *number* or *figure* or *pound.* Its use is restricted to a symbol similar to an asterisk.

If an unusual abbreviation is used, an explanation of the abbreviation should be made immediately following its first appearance in the report.

Some abbreviations have more than a single meaning in one or different fields. Dual meaning is confusing and certainly should be avoided unless each abbreviation is defined and used for the same

* R. C. Weast, ed.-in-chief, 45th ed., Chem. Rubber Pub. Co., Cleveland, Ohio, 1964.

word or group of words throughout a single report. For example abbreviations that have had more than one meaning:

BT for *bathythermograph* and *blue tetrazolium*

BP for *before the present, blood pressure,* and *boiling point*

H for *sorbitol, histidine,* and *hydrogen*

PNH for *reduced pyridine nucleotide* and *paroxymal nocturnal hemoglobinuria*

TCP for *trichlorophenoxyacetic acid, trichlorophenol,* and *tricresyl phosphate*

IV for *intravenous* and Roman numeral *4*

Then again a turnabout of this confusion is created when several different abbreviations have been used for the same word or symbol, such as, CMB, PCMB, pCMB, *p*ClHgBe for *p*-chloromercuribenzoate, and T, TX, and THY for *thyroxin.*

Several abbreviations that have been found in common usage, such as TNT, DDT, ACTH, TV, and IQ have become a part of the language and are perhaps better known than their parent expressions. Certain others, such as ADP, and ATP (adenosine di- and triphosphate), DPN and TPN (di- and triphosphopyridine nucleotide), and DNA and RNA (deoxyribonucleic acid and ribonucleic acid), are well-known, at least in biochemistry, medicine and related fields. But even such a well-known abbreviation as ADP has had different meanings, such as *adenosine diphosphate, automatic data processing,* and *ammonium dihydrogen phosphate.* See Appendix A for the commonly accepted list of biochemical abbreviations suggested in "Directions for Abstractors" by Chemical Abstracts Service and "Style Manual for Biological Journals" by the American Institute of Biological Sciences.

In view of this confusion and lack of standardization if there is doubt, spell out.

Abbreviations in the title of a paper are not used, mainly because if this were translated into a foreign language an undefined or uncommon abbreviation could lead to all kinds of headaches. Ordinarily a sentence should not begin with an abbreviation.

Spelling

For nonscientific words "Webster's Seventh New Collegiate Dictionary" or any up-to-date dictionary for that matter is an undisputable authority. However, new words have come into use and new spellings have become common, especially in science, without the authority of entries in a standard dictionary to support them. However, the best authority in the chemical field is "Hawley's Technical Speller." *

Spelling errors mar an otherwise well-written paper. They reflect unfavorably on the writer, create doubt about the care and accuracy with which the author wrote his report, and they distract the reader. Technical terms, familiar to the writer and written in a hasty scrawl, are unfamiliar to the typist, and the writer is inviting error. This will be an embarrassment to the author, who might not even find these very same errors while proofreading. Careful proofreading is a must. Words that somehow seem wrong should be looked up and corrected if need be.

Only one word ends in *sede,* supersede; only three words end in *ceed,* exceed, proceed, succeed; all other words of this class end in *cede,* concede, recede, etc.

In the following words, "Webster" sanctions the shortened spelling. These are acceptable in all writing, even formal reports.

Preferred	Alternative, Not Preferred
anesthetic	anaesthetic
buret	burette
catalog	catalogue
distil (distilled)	distill
employe	employee
enzymic	enzymatic
gage	gauge
hemoglobin	haemoglobin
homolog	homologue
levo	laevo
mold	mould
pharmacopeia	pharmacopoeia
pipet	pipette
pellicle	pellicule
sulfur	sulphur
viscometer	viscosimeter

* G. G. Hawley and A. W. Hawley, Reinhold Pub. Corp., New York, 1955.

But such shorthand forms as *altho, enuf, tho, nite,* and *thru* should not appear in formal writing.

The conventions, rules, guides, and opinions in this chapter represent current conservative technical writing. As times change these items are most susceptible to change, especially trade names and spelling. The personality, age, and nationality of the author is often revealed by his use of such conventions.

CHAPTER 9 *Good Grammar Is Essential*

Technically trained people recognize the need for correct grammatical form in well-organized reports. Therefore only a few points of grammar will be mentioned. The report writer should consult "Webster" or a textbook on grammar for more detailed help. An authoritative reference such as H. W. Fowler's "A Dictionary of Modern English Usage" (Oxford University Press, New York, 1958) gives confidence to a writer, no matter how inexperienced. Another good reference is R. P. Turner's "Grammar Review for Technical Writers" (Holt, Rinehart, and Winston, Inc., New York, 1964).

Verb Tenses

A report should be consistent in the use of verb tenses. Adequate selection of tense conveys to the reader the relative timing of the items being discussed. The present tense is used for generalizations and references to conditions that do not change; observations and experiments are written in the past tense. The future tense is used to describe planned work.

The subjunctive form of a verb, expressing an improbable condition or one contrary to fact, usually does not lend itself to scientific writing. However, it is found occasionally in speculative articles on technical subjects.

Voice

The passive voice should be used sparingly in technical reports; it requires extra words and may not convey the exact meaning.

Compare "The synapse liberates acetylcholine" with "Acetylcholine is produced by the synapse." The passive here requires two more words and 25% more space. "It was found to have had" is simply, in the active voice, "It had." This awkward construction does dominate a great deal of technical writing, especially that emanating from government bureaus and business offices. The writer should keep the active voice in his report unless he has a good reason for departing from it, or unless there is no real advantage over the passive in his report.

But a blanket ban on the passive robs the author of more freedom of expression. Technical writing is generally impersonal writing. The active form, "I dialyzed the solution" has no real advantage over the passive, "The solution was dialyzed." The active voice is preferred when the identity of the observer or doer of the experiment is significant. For example,

Good: Knight gives a detailed report,
Poor: A detailed report was given by Knight,
Good: Black and Brown believe the literature inadequate,
Poor: It is believed that the literature is inadequate.

In general, the passive voice is used to excess in reporting experimental work, and readers appreciate the action relief afforded by a frequent use of active verbs.

Modifiers

Words, phrases, and even clauses are often introduced into a sentence to modify, that is, to limit or tell something more about particular words or statements. Modifiers should be placed as near as possible to the words they modify. "I decided when I had finished the titration to quit" leaves the reader uncertain whether "when I had finished the titration" is meant to modify "decided" or "to quit." "When I had finished the titration I decided to quit" or "I decided to quit when I had finished the titration" resolves the confusion by placing the modifying clause in an unambiguous position.

The author should avoid long series of modifying words such as "under-jet, fuel-gas manifolds. It is better to say fuel-gas manifold with under jets." The writer's real problem is to avoid clumsiness and absurdity through a careless placing of modifiers.

Participles

Most scientists seem to have a penchant for dangling participles. Although there are occasional sentences where an unattached participle does not appear illiterate, it is only fair to the report reader to recast loose cases of dangling participles.

Participles are misused in many sentences where the participial phrase should form a logical continuation of the preceding thought. In the following examples the participial clause is misused because it makes an additional statement that has no clear relation to an antecedent.

The stones were composed of cholesterol, *occurring* chiefly in the lower half of the large intestine. Much of it is translucent, the round cells *being* one-half micron in diameter.

Sometimes in analyzing a sentence it is difficult to distinguish a participle used as an adjective from a passive verb. The decision rests on whether the participle modifies the subject, as a predicate adjective with a linking verb, or whether it describes an action.

Passive voice: The polyester at that temperature was flowing.
Predicate adjective: The polyester was flowing but viscous.

When used as an adjective, a participle should refer clearly to some particular noun or pronoun.

Avoiding the habitual phrases and jargon of your field, you use simple words and only technical terms. (*Avoiding* modifies *you.*)

There should be no reasonable doubt of what is modified. A modifying participle *dangles* or is *misrelated* when it seems to refer to nothing, or to a word the writer does not intend.

Misrelated: Walking about the grounds, several of the rust-resistant white pines can be seen.
Proper: While walking about the grounds, one can see several of the rust-resistant white pines.

Because the reader expects participles to refer to the subject of the following clause, he is disappointed. It is not so much a matter of meaning, for the sentence with a dangling participle is rarely ambiguous (though it may be amusing). It is rather a matter of accurate expression.

The participle-as-adjective should not be confused with the participle in a phrase which relates to the whole sentence rather than to a particular word. Some of these phrases are common:

Generally speaking, these cells are gram-negative.
Beginning with C in Chart 4, the trend toward resistance can be seen.
Letting x represent inventory at time t, solve Equation 3 for K.
Looking through the telescope, the stars were larger.
Judging by present standards, these papers are valuable.

The use of participles and verbal nouns in English seems to be increasing, but there is a tendency for some report writers to use participles in constructions that they would never use in speaking. A subordinate clause would be more natural.

The distillation was going slowly, *being heated* by an alcohol burner. (Leave out *being*.)

In many sentences a participle may be replaced by a defining relative clause with a slight gain in emphasis and possibly clarity.

A test plank *sloping* (that slopes) gently toward the floor is satisfactory.

Gerund

A gerund, or verbal noun, is the form of the verb ending in *-ing* when used as a noun. It has the same form as the present participle but differs in use.

Gerund: Running a laboratory offers opportunities for sound judgment.
Participle: Running around the laboratory, the rabbit found the door.

Gerunds are often used in phrases:

In starting the generator, they blew the main fuse.
This is the best compound for *stopping water leaks.*

The gerund phrase should modify the word the writer intends it to:

> *Misrelated: After arriving at the decision,* a vote was taken. (*A vote* did not arrive *at the decision.*)
> *Correct:* After arriving at the decision, the committee took a vote.
> *Dangling gerund:* Before *dumping* the beaker, the sink must be clear.
> *Correct:* Before *dumping* the beaker, make sure the sink is clear.

Emphasizing the verbal phase of a word gives economy and force to a report.

> *Strong:* In *revising* the first draft, a writer can check the spelling.
> *Weak:* In the *revising* of the first draft, a writer can check the spelling.

Antecedents

A pronoun refers to something without naming it, so that its meaning (except for an indefinite pronoun) is complete by its reference to some other word or group of words called its *antecedent.* This fact makes the proper use of pronouns more complicated than the use of other words, which name and so refer directly to persons or things or actions or qualities. The personal and relative pronouns are further complicated by having a separate form for the objective case; nouns do not. The reader of a report can see clearly the form and reference of pronouns. The writer needs especially to watch his pronouns. In revising a paper he should make sure that they are accurate in form and in reference. Testing the reference of pronouns is one of the specific jobs of revising a report.

It, this, and *these* are most frequently used with doubtful antecedents.

> *Wrong: This* shows that the pipes were rusty.
> *Better: This color* shows that the pipes were rusty.
> *Wrong:* The word "chemistry" means little to a child. Yet it deals with materials in our homes, offices, food, automobiles, and clothing.

The word *chemistry* could replace the pronoun *it* in the third sentence, so that the reader would know that *it* refers to *chemistry,* not the *child.*

Use a singular pronoun to refer to such antecedents as: *man,*

woman, person, one, anyone, anybody, someone, somebody, every,
everyone, everybody, each, kind, sort, either, neither, no one, none,
nobody.

> *Every one* of the mice drinks from the contaminated dish.
> *It* learns quickly.

English has no single pronoun to mean he-or-she, so the mascu-
line is always used.

Two or more antecedents joined by *and* are referred to by a
plural pronoun; two or more singular antecedents joined by *or* or
nor are referred to by a singular pronoun. If one of two antecedents
joined by *or* is singular and one plural, the pronoun agrees with
the nearer. For instance:

> When boys and girls enter college, *they* find it different from high school.
> When a boy or girl works on his thesis, *he* finds the library convenient.
> The typists or a secretary works here. *She* needs more equipment.

The use of an indefinite antecedent may confuse the reader for
a moment and at the same time break the trend of thought desired
by the author, for example:

> *Wrong:* The gage was attached to the boiler, but it was found to be de-
> fective.
> *Right:* The gage, which was found to be defective, was attached to the
> boiler.

A writer should avoid vague general references by pronouns without definite antecedents.

> *Wrong:* Table A shows the rate of survival. This is a test that can be
> measured.
> *Better:* Table A shows the rate of survival. Determining the survival rate
> is a test that can be measured.

Care should be taken in the use of the relative pronouns *that,*
what, whatever, which, of which, who, whose, whom, and *whoever.*

> *Who* refers to a person.
> *That* refers to a person, animal, or thing.
> *Which* refers to an animal or thing.
> *What* usually has no definite antecedent.

Use *who* and *which* where the meaning is *and he, and it, for he,* and *for it. That* and *which* may refer to a person or a thing, but there is a distinction in their use. *That* defines and restricts; *which* explains and supplements. For example:

Wrong: Statistical reports *which* are poorly written should not be published.
Right: Statistical reports *that* are poorly written should not be published.

In the foregoing example, it was not intended to state that *all* statistical reports were poorly written and *none* should be published. Therefore the restrictive *that* should be used.

A relative pronoun with a plural antecedent requires a plural verb. Such as:

The hospital purchased *microscopes that had been used* in the tropics.

The verb agrees with the subject, not with the nearest predicate noun.

Wrong: The beauty of the numerous lines and curves *lie* in the designs.
Right: The beauty of the numerous lines and curves *lies* in the designs.

In measurements and amounts a plural noun is often followed by a singular verb. For instance:

Ninety-eight cents is the purchase price of the flask.
The last five years has been a period of rioting.
Thirty-six inches is a yard.

When the writer means a group as a whole, a collective noun takes a singular verb and singular pronoun; when the writer means the individuals of the group, the noun takes a plural verb or pronoun. For instance:

Ninety-eight cents were counted out carefully on the counter. Ninety-eight cents was the price.
Ten milliliters were mixed dropwise. Ten milliliters was needed per mole.

Here is a list of typical collective nouns:

army	company	group	physics
athletics	contents	herd	politics
audience	couple	jury	public
band	crowd	majority	remainder
barracks	dozen	mankind	rest, meaning remainder
bunch	economics	mathematics	row
children	flock	news	scissors
class	gang	number	tactics
committee	government	offspring	team

In the sentence, "The committee is able to vote," *committee* is regarded as a unit and is thus singular. But in the sentence, "The committee were at odds over the vote," the individual members couldn't agree, so *committee* is plural.

Corporation can be treated either as singular or plural, depending on whether the writer regards it as a whole or has the individual partners or stockholders in mind. Generally firms use the plural in their correspondence and brochures. They write, "Write to us" or "Send for our complete pamphlet." "Write to me" or "Send for my complete pamphlet" would be confusing and humorous, and "Write to it" or "Send for its complete pamphlet" is clearly wrong.

It is equally correct to write "General Motors have revised their advertising" or "General Motors has revised their advertising." Some grammarians do not like the second of these examples because it combines a singular verb and a plural pronoun. This mixed form is widely used by great writers, including those who wrote our Constitution (Article 1, Section 5):

> Each house shall keep a journal of *its* proceedings, and from time to time publish the same, excepting such parts as may in *their* judgment require secrecy.

Data is a plural form which may take either a singular or plural verb. Most of us find the real singular of the word strange, for example, "an unpleasant datum." Social scientists commonly use *data* as a singular. They refer to "the data shows" and "it" and talk about "much data" and "little data." These singular constructions are permissible if they are not followed by a plural verb. However, in the physical sciences, and in technical report writing, *data* is treated as plural. It is not enough to use a plural verb, but if an author writes "the data are," then he should refer to "they," and say "these data" and "many data." An author should not write "much of the data are now updated" or "little data are here." Examples are as follows:

These data are mixed in the notebook. *They* show a downward trend.
A piece of data is missing from this notebook. *It* is lost.

Obviously a collective should not be treated as both singular and plural in the same context. For example:

The *public was* organized and immediately sent out *its* (not *their*) deputies.

Split Infinitive

The word order in which an adverb comes between the *to* and the verb is a *split infinitive*. For example:

Split: to rapidly boil; *not split:* to boil rapidly.

Awkward split infinitives are poor writing and ought to be revised.

Awkward: After awhile I was able to, although not very accurately, distinguish the blue solutions from the green ones.
Improved: After awhile I was able to distinguish—though not very accurately—the blue solutions from the green ones.

Since the adverb modifies the verb, its natural position seems to be next to the verb. But sometimes this construction gives a forced distortion, and it is better then to split the infinitive. For example:

Some of the hailstones failed completely to melt before they reached the ground.

Does this sentence mean that the hailstones did not melt at all or that just a little ice remained when the melting stopped? In this example, the adverb can be placed after the infinitive *to melt* without seriously affecting the euphony or altering the meaning of the sentence. Then consider this:

The average layman fails fully to understand scientific phenomena that he encounters daily.

Laying aside the question of clumsy alliteration, doesn't this sentence mean that the layman fails to fully understand? Here the problem cannot be dodged merely by putting the adverb after the infinitive, which yields an ambiguity—"fully scientific phenomena."

Certainly the above sentence can be recast, but just what is there to be gained? Split the infinitive. The sentence is then clear and smooth.

Most split constructions can be avoided in one way or another. All but the most stuffy writers will admit that there are occasional instances where the split infinitive is not only the simplest construction, but is almost unavoidable. Other examples:

> The voltage should be adjusted to just balance the potential drop in resistance.
> Over the next decade, the company expects to more than double its net sales.

If weight of authority amounts to anything, it is best to quote the late George Bernard Shaw, who wrote to an editor:

"There is a busybody on your staff who devotes a lot of his time to chasing split infinitives. Every good literary craftsman splits his infinitives when the sense demands it. I call for the immediate dismissal of the pedant. It is of no consequence whether he decides to go quickly or quickly to go or to quickly go. The important thing is that he should go at once."

An English woman would say, "It's very generous of her giving me the water color." An American would have said, "It's very generous of her to give me the water color."

Road signs read KEEP TO THE RIGHT EXCEPT TO PASS. Contemporary American English is showing a marked tendency to use the infinitive.

It is increasingly popular to express the exact meaning only by putting an adverb between the verb and the *to*. "Joe hoped to at least triple his investment" is not expressed in "Joe hoped at least to triple his investment" because in the second sentence "at least" may modify *hoped,* not *triple*. And writers, especially report writers, would much prefer to split an infinitive than to run the risk of being misunderstood.

But an author should avoid dangling infinitives, such as:

Dangling: To grow fine sweet peas, strings should support the plants.
Better: To grow fine sweet peas, support the plants by string.

Terminal Preposition

Another literary taboo, which, happily, is fast becoming discredited, is the precept against ending a sentence with a preposition. The late Sir Winston Churchill scribbled the following cryptic note on the margin of a manuscript he was sent to read: "This is the sort of English up with which I will not put."

Sir. H. Walton's humor is pungently expressed in: "Hanging is the worst use a man can be put to."

Then there is the story of the nursemaid who managed to collect four prepositions at the end of a sentence: "What did you choose that book to be read to out of for?"

The preposition at the end of a sentence is so generally the normal word order that the real danger is in clumsiness trying to avoid it, for instance:

Tell me what it is to which you disagree (disagree to).
To whatever source may be appealed, he will argue. (appealed to ....)

There is no reason for hesitating to let a preposition fall at the end if natural idiom and rhythm place it there. Here are some examples of effective idiomatic usage:

What is this value for?
Democracy is certainly a way of life worth fighting for.
Now faith is the substance of things hoped for. (Hebrews 11:1)
It was apparent that the engineer knew what he was talking about.
... the thousand shocks that flesh is heir to. (Hamlet)

Charles Ferguson wrote in his book "Say It With Words," *
"One might even come up with a style that cultivates instead of avoids prepositions. They are pesky things at best—always in and around and under foot, things that we turn up at the end of sen-

* Alfred A. Knopf, New York, 1959.

tences with. Over against the tendency to escape their toils let us set the practice for a spell of learning and wooing prepositions, studding our speech deliberately with them. This can abolish our fear of them—or at least help to."

Subject Nominative

A mischoice of subject nominative gives a sentence wordiness and lack of clearness and force. Such as:

> *Weak:* The principal use of monocalcium phosphate is in the manufacture of baking chemicals.
> *Better:* Monocalcium phosphate is used chiefly in making baking chemicals.

Some writers forget their subject nominative before they finish the sentence. For instance:

> The flow is tremendous and is said to be excellent for drinking.

The flow of the spring is so many gallons a minute. It is the water, presumably, not the flow, that is excellent.

Logical Analysis

Some sentences cannot stand an examination of logical analysis; their writers have failed to keep in mind the relations of all parts of the sentence to one another. Here are some examples which were found in reports:

> This type of filter will fulfill the health requirements as well as lessen the need for a long life.

What was meant was that because of the type of filter it did not need a long life; what the sentence seemed to say was that there was no need for a person having a long life.

> The red berries induce violent illness in man, which is no hardship, since they are not at all palatable.

What was meant was that because the berries are sour it is no hardship to refrain from eating them; what was said was that the illness induced by eating them is no hardship.

Often readers forget the subject of a report but remember the author for his flubs. The writer may be quoted, not for his subject, but for his humorous style. A serious report writer does not wish to become a humorist to his readers.

An author should avoid such phrases "elute the spots," "extract the paper," because in chromatography one elutes or extracts *the substance* from the paper. An author should not write of "mixing the tubes," "titrating the tubes," or "distilling the flasks," but the *fractions* or *contents* of the tubes and flasks.

Jargon

Jargon is the slang or shorthand of technical language. Many sciences have manufactured words by adding -*ate*, a suffix indicating the result of a process: *filtrate* is that which has been filtered. And there are the inventions *supernate, centrifugate,* and *dialysate.* To add confusion some prefixes produce jargon: *preincubate, prewarmed, retested, inflammable, nonflammable, noninflammable, unincubate.* There is a wide practice of concocting verbs from adjectives by adding -*ize; epimerize, finalize, ionize, isomerize, personalize, racemize, solubilize, metalize, ozonize,* and from the business field *percentagewise.* Other new compound words have been formed by adding *re-* as a prefix: *regenerate, rehydrolyze, redissolve, reincubate.* Some of these words are incomprehensible: *derivatize, grignardize, solidize, sonicate.*

Medicine is filled with compounded words: *appendectomy, cardiectomy, celiosalpingectomy, ganglionectomy* are only a few formed by adding -*ectomy.* Then there are the words which begin with *hyper-* or *hypo-,* or end in -*glossia,* -*itis,* etc.

Some scientists use intransitive verbs, which do not take an object or have the passive voice, as if they were transitive. For example, one cannot "react phenol with sodium hydroxide," or state that "phenol was reacted with bromine."

For more on laboratory jargon "Style Guide for Chemists" by L. F. Fieser and M. Fieser (Reinhold Pub. Corp., New York, 1960) is good. Also, "Style Manual for Biological Journals," (*Am. Inst. Biol. Sci.,* 200 P Street, NW, Washington 6, D.C.) and "How to Write

Reports," by C. D. Linton (Harper and Bros., New York, 1954) discuss the use of jargon in technical writing.

Jargon is often inaccurate and pompous and may conceal the real facts. "Fully cognizant of," for example, may mean anything from "I have heard of this before" to "I am now frantically studying the subject for the first time." The report which notes that "the agreement was then consummated" may mean that and may not. It may mean only that the agreement was signed, or approved; but the word *consummate* actually means to bring to completion or perfection. To write, "The chairman interposed an objection directed against the initial instance" instead of "the chairman objected to the first point" is pompous and the act of a skilled "jargoneer."

Adverbial expressions easily develop into what might be called personal jargon, the unthinking habit of an individual writer. In an effort to avoid the mental concentration necessary for the selection of a more exact link, a writer may become addicted to a phrase like "in this connection" or a word like "thus" or "however."

Jargon habitually employs the passive voice. "It has been shown" instead of "The data showed." "It will be appreciated if your report is referred to this office" instead of "Please send me your report." "It is believed that a favorable economic situation will be developed by the prompt implementation of these recommendations" instead of "I believe it will be profitable for us to carry out these proposals," or "Doing as suggested appears profitable." The thought behind the expression is as vague and pompous as the writing.

Clichés

Clichés, like jargon, are situation-produced rather than thought-produced, but unlike jargon, which is inherently bad, clichés are only worn out. When they were original they had an effective vividness, but overuse made them hackneyed, producing no effect on the reader.

For the technical writer, figurative language (clichés), no matter how fresh, is of limited usefulness. To say that a certain event "sparked" a violent reaction is all right if the circumstances make

the image quite valid, but the more straightforward verb "caused"
is safer. Sir Winston Churchill used exquisite images with fresh,
effective figures of speech, but the average technical report writer
must avoid these fetching figures.

The number of clichés established over the years is incalculable:
"diamond in the rough," "grim determination," "tight as a drum,"
"shadow of a doubt," "last-ditch stand," "new frontiers," "terrific,"
"with vigor," "the great society," "extremism," "high as a kite."
The report writer can follow a simple rule: if a figure of speech
comes easily to mind and sounds familiar, forget it.

Pedantry

Pedantry, so far as it is exhibited in word choice, may be felt
as pomposity or precocity. Some writers use their vocabularies
partly to convey thought and partly to display their own erudition.
When you read, "Following the obsequies, the sorrowing relatives
repaired to their domiciles," you probably have a suspicion you
would not like the author. Language should be treated with kind-
ness and understanding, not prissy fastidiousness. An overreverent
attitude toward the more flexible rules of grammar is another mark
of the pedant, and suggests a rigidity of mind and a lack of real
understanding. Occasionally it is better to split an infinitive than
to mince about the problem awkwardly, and often a preposition
is exactly what a sentence should end with. The pedant always
writes "The motor hardly had begun" instead of "The motor had
hardly begun" in order to avoid interrupting the compound verb,
which is a good enough general principle, but not always the rule
to follow. A sentence should not be awkward, but smooth and
natural.

These comments should not be interpreted as suggesting that a
short, vague word is better than a long precise one. "To inculcate"
means a great deal more than "to put in" or "to add." In a recent
technical journal an author was pedantic and pompous when he
wrote, "Indeed, evidence for brain plasticity would seem to be propaedeutic and essential for the sound development of research on
many major questions of brain-behavior relations." Or was he only

using the word, *propaedeutic,* with precisely the meaning he wanted? Could he have used "introductory" or "preparatory" just as well?

The technical report writer, in avoiding pedantry, must not conform to the modern tendency to reduce vocabularies as well as men to the level of the commonplace, but he must *think* for himself.

CHAPTER 10 *Put Punch in Your Writing*

G. G. HAWLEY
Executive Editor, Reinhold Book Division

In technical report writing it is unquestionably true that *what* is stated is more important than *how* it is stated. Yet no matter how scientific verbal communication may be, its purpose is to impart facts and ideas clearly, forcefully and exactly. This end cannot be achieved without some degree of attention to the mode of expression. For those who may not be convinced of the importance of *how* ideas are presented, we offer two examples, leaving the reader to decide which statement in each case communicates the author's idea more vividly. The reasons for this greater effectiveness comprise the content of this chapter.

> Roll on, thou dark and deep blue ocean, roll!
> Roll, roll on, thou dark and deep blue ocean!

> Down dropped the wind, the sails dropped down.
> The wind dropped down, the sails dropped down.

Most attempts to offer advice on writing involve such oversimplifications as: "Select simple words, short sentences, observe the rules of grammar and punctuation, and write as clearly and forcefully as possible." How often have you read statements like this? These generalities are of scant help when you are chewing on a pencil and wondering how to start transforming your mass of notes and data into an effective report.

Because everyone speaks and reads the English language daily, there is a tendency to regard writing as something that requires no special ability and that anybody can do well. Actually a technique is involved in good writing, just as in hitting a baseball or sawing a board. There are a few who are fortunate enough to be born with an ability to write well, but most of us have to work at the expression of our ideas if they are to be understood and remembered.

Style

There are no definite rules of procedure for writing an effective report. The grammar of a language reflects the usage of that language; the rules come into being by an inductive process. Knowledge of these rules is necessary for understanding the mechanics of expression, and it is possible to be very definite about them. But one may know all the ins and outs of gammar and syntax and still be an ineffective writer. The technique of expressing ideas clearly and effectively is less precise and more subtle than rules can define; it is not only the most creative part of writing but also the most useful part. This creative process is usually called *style*.

Carl Sandburg once said, "My style is my face—you may not like it, but for God's sake don't change it!" More recently, Henry Seidel Canby compared style with happiness: "Everyone recognizes it, everyone describes it, but no two people agree as to its exact nature." Style is the writer's own distinctive way of expressing his personality in vocabulary, sentence structure, and idiom. If we compare styles of various authors we can detect a broad variety of moods and effects. What a difference there is between an accurate expression of thought and individuality and the careless stringing together of words that perhaps achieves intelligibility, but nothing more!

Style is a product of *feeling* as well as of *thinking*. It is always hard to establish regulations about anything having a large component of subjectivity. For example, few infallible rules for word order exist; proper positioning of elements within a sentence depends largely on which arrangement is the clearest and most effective in a given case.

Clarity and effectiveness often depend on a feeling for rhythm, balance, contrast and suspense that is almost impossible to impart.

This feeling, or word sense, is definitely capable of being developed by conscious effort and attention.

In this book, frequent reference is made to *good writing,* which is not to be taken to mean *fine writing*—the over-formal, self-conscious effort to impress readers with unusual words and stilted phrases. Good writing has none of these useless and turgid departures from common sense and good taste. It is simple, direct, and literal; but it requires an understanding of the technique of arranging the sentence elements effectively, and particularly an awareness of the possibilities inherent in word order. Since much of the application is subjective, and depends on a writer's own perception of the lights and shadows of emphasis, the various points are presented here as suggestions, rather than rules. Each case must be decided on its merits.

For a study of distinctive style, we recommend these books to technical report writers:

(1) King James version of the New Testament for the majesty of its rhythm and dignity and simplicity of diction.

(2) Wiener, N., "Cybernetics," 2nd ed., MIT Press, Cambridge, Mass., 1961.

(3) Beveridge, W. I. B., "The Art of Scientific Investigation," rev. ed., W. W. Norton and Co., New York, 1957 (paperback, Vantage, 1957).

(4) Shapley, H., "Of Stars and Men," rev. ed., Beacon Press, Boston, 1964.

(5) Bridgman, P. W., "The Way Things Are," Viking Press, Inc., New York, 1961.

(6) Strunk, Jr., W., and White, W. B., "Elements of Style," Macmillan, 1959.

Expression

Natural expression is usually simple and brief. In technical reports, simplicity and brevity delight the reader, particularly when the writing shows a disciplined selection and order. When brevity is used merely for its own sake, style suffers and the writing is underdeveloped and thin. The skillful writer will use an ornamental flow of expression where it relieves monotony, and will lengthen certain sections of his report where emphasis seems justified. But word economy, used with discretion, is a powerful aid to literary style. As a writer develops a good style, he learns to distinguish between economy and abruptness. A graceful style shows a sense of the significant.

Much weak writing is the result of arbitrary rules "remembered" from high-school days, most of which have little validity, if indeed they ever existed. English is fluid; words and word combinations should be regarded as plastic materials to be molded into the finished structure by the writer's ingenuity, not prefabricated units to be bolted together with punctuation, as in legalistic or "boiler plate" prose. Writing that lacks balance and emphasis is much like inadequately seasoned food: it is there and it will nourish you, but you will hate eating it. People will read your reports because they have to; but your ideas will not stand out, and the whole thing will be a chore for everybody concerned.

George Herbert Palmer's idea of expression, which is still true sixty years later, is as follows: "Good English is exact English. . . . Too frequently words signify nothing in particular. . . . The first business of everyone who would train himself in language is to articulate his thought, to know definitely what he wishes to say, and then pick those words which compel the reader to think of this and only this. For such a purpose, two words are often better than three. . . . *Something like* what we mean must never be counted equivalent to *what we mean*. And if we are not sure of the meaning of our word we must pause until we are sure."

Unity

A sentence which conveys clearly the single idea or meaning which the writer intends to convey possesses the quality of unity. Use of words involves the contruction of sentences. It is true that ideas are conveyed by single words—tree, beauty, death—but the communication of information is by sentences: "The tree is beautiful" or "The tree is dead." The need for the proper relationships among words in a sentence poses numerous composition problems. Effective composition demands an appreciation of grammar, as well as an understanding of the psychological factors. It is essential for the writer to keep the reader's needs and knowledge constantly in mind.

The claim is sometimes made that the statement of two thoughts of equal importance actually constitutes two sentences; for example:

> The insecticide was effective, and there were tremoring, convulsions, and paralysis symptomatic of poisoning.

Whether or not this sentence is really two sentences masquerading as one is an academic question. The construction is certainly legitimate. Esthetic and practical considerations will determine whether the two intimately related thoughts are to be expressed as a single, fluid sentence or separated into two short, staccato sentences.

Unity is not synonymous with singleness. There are few sentences, except in primers, that say only one thing. Unity must always be interpreted in terms of completeness, which depends upon context. If the sentence contains one manifest major action or fact plus all subordinate related ideas, then that sentence is unified. Fragmentary sentences are commoner in most technical reports than overcrowded ones. Consider the following:

> In a 200-cc round-bottomed flask place 32 (0.3 mole) of purified toluene. The round-bottomed flask should be provided with a reflux condenser. To the flask add 19.0 cc of cp concentrated sulfuric acid. Add a clay boiling chip to the mixture. Heat the mixture over an asbestos gauze. Shake the flask constantly with a rotary motion.

These sentences are surely single, but they are not unified, because they present in pieces ideas which are not of equal importance and which all relate to a single thought: getting the substances in the flask to be heated. A well-unified sentence would put all these ideas together in a single statement:

> In a 200-cc round-bottomed flask provided with a reflux condenser place 32 (0.3 mole) of purified toluene and 19.0 cc of cp concentrated sulfuric acid, add a clay boiling chip and heat the mixture on an asbestos gauze while shaking constantly with a rotary motion.

The difference between these two versions shows that it is important to write each sentence in accordance with a definite plan; don't just let sentences grow.

An author should show the relationship between ideas by using exact conjunctions, avoiding repeated use of *and* and *so*. For example:

> The mixture was not shaken, so the nitrobenzene layer did not react completely.

The sentence is improved and more united:

> Because the mixture was not shaken, the nitrobenzene layer did not react completely.

The important thought should be in independent constructions, subordinate thoughts in dependent constructions. The direction of thought should not be changed more than once within a sentence. For example:

> The operation was disrupted, for it was known the electricity was limited, for the shutoff was long anticipated.

The sentence can be improved thus:

> The operation was disrupted, for it was known the electricity was limited; the shutoff was long anticipated.

An author should avoid overlapping constructions in unifying a sentence. Relative pronouns, such as *who, which, that,* etc., and subordinating conjunctions link two ideas, the second of which depends on the first. When this construction piles up, third units depending on the second, fourth units on the third, etc.; the effect is to put the reader to sleep, or draw him away from the main point of the sentence. Unity is destroyed because the sentence is made to say several things, all of which overlap.

Emphasis

One of the most difficult and important aspects of writing is emphasis—saying something so that it stands out like a lighted match in a black-out. Arrange the material so that one idea dominates. The word "arrange" here refers primarily to the position of the word in the sentence. English is basically a language of position, so that it makes a great difference *where* you put your strongest words, and *how* you arrange the others in relation to them.

As a general rule for all writing—sentence, paragraph, and whole reports—the end is the position of greatest importance, and the beginning the next. The weaker, contributing ideas should go in the middle.

(1) The acid catalyzed the reaction, and caustic stopped it.

Whether the foregoing sentence is written as a compound sentence of two coordinate clauses or as two separate sentences, the two statements are related and intended to carry equal weight. The following constructions convey the same information, but with slight changes in emphasis.

(2) The acid and caustic controlled the reaction.
(3) The caustic arrested and overcame the catalysis of the acid.

Now see what happens when first one, and then the other, of the two clauses in sentence 1 is made subordinate.

(4) The acid catalyzed the reaction, which the caustic stopped.
(5) The caustic stopped the reaction that the acid catalyzed.

The two sentences 4 and 5 convey the same idea, but with different emphasis. In the first, attention is centered upon the action of the acid. The subordinate clause, introduced by *which* and preceded by a comma, does not *define* the reaction, but merely makes a further statement about it. Such a subordinate clause is called a *nondefining* clause; it is properly introduced by *which*. In sentence 5, the principal statement deals with the action of the caustic on a *particular* reaction identified by a defining clause, which is here introduced by *that*. Attention can be focused upon *reaction* by shifting from the active to the passive voice.

(6) The caustic stopped the reaction that the acid catalyzed.
(7) The reaction catalyzed by the acid was stopped by the caustic.

There are many ways of saying *almost* the same thing—in the words of Palmer previously quoted, *"something like* what we mean."

The illustrations given by no means exhaust the possible variations of this one sentence.

A sentence can be made to convey more information related to the principal thought by the introduction of modifying words and phrases, for example:

> (8) The reaction of acetaldehyde to replace acetone, which the sulfuric acid catalyzed at 30°C, was promptly stopped by the addition of an equivalent of caustic.

Now the compositional problems begin to multiply rapidly. As the possibilities of communication increase, so do the difficulties of construction. Qualifying clauses and phrases tend to extend the separation between the subject and its verb. They often weaken the connection between a relative pronoun and its antecedent. They raise questions of precedence and comparative importance. The more information you pack into a sentence, the more decisions you must make regarding emphasis, word order, punctuation, and even choice of words. These decisions should result in a sentence that is easy to read, unambiguous, and completely self-consistent—in short, a sentence that has emphasis, unity, and coherence.

Coherence

Unity demands that each sentence make a single, complete statement: coherence demands that all the elements of each sentence work together to say it. Some ideas cohere so naturally that little skill is needed to make their relationship apparent, and others need every device of language and grammar to make their pattern of logical coherence clear. It is probably harder to achieve sentence coherence than unity and emphasis combined.

"Coherence is the traditional name for *relationship, connection, and consecutiveness....* Carefully thinking over material before beginning to write should help prepare a coherent paper, especially if some sort of plan, arranging the different stages in a natural and sensible order, is drawn up. The writer must sit as reader, go over his copy as impersonally as he can to see if what he has written not only hangs together for him but will, so far as he can judge, hang together for those he wants to read it. He should ask himself, 'Is the relation between these statements clear? Can a reader pass from this sentence to the next, from this paragraph to the next, without feeling a break?'

"A natural arrangement of material is not enough for this; there must often be signs of the relationship between sentences and paragraphs." (Porter G. Perrin, "Writer's Guide and Index to English," Scott, Foresman, 1942.)

Normal and Inverted Word Order

A brief look at the anatomy of style may aid the writer in acquiring the ability to observe and appreciate the writing of others and then to apply these techniques to his own work. Some of the illustrative examples used are synthetic, and some have been taken from actual manuscripts. These examples are the most important part of this chapter and should be read slowly and thoughtfully.

Normal: Automation is the key concept of modern industrial processing.
(1) (2) (3)

This kind of sentence is technically known as *simple,* which means that it contains only one verb. In this case the verb (2) is of the copulative type (all forms of *to be*) which implies that the subject (1) is intimately related to, or identical with, the noun (3) or adjective which follows (called the *complement*). Other types of sentences have two or more main (or coordinate) clauses (compound sentence), or one main clause and one or more subordinate clauses (complex sentence). In addition to copulative verbs there are *transitive* verbs, which are followed by a noun or its equivalent, called the object; and *intransitive* verbs, which are complete in themselves.

In the foregoing example, the subject (1) comes first, followed immediately by the verb (2) and by the complement (3). This natural arrangement is called *normal order.* As its name suggests, it is the usual or regular way of constructing a sentence. But normal order is often the least emphatic, and therefore the least effective. Expression may be effectively sharpened simply by altering the order of these three elements, resulting in *inverted* order. This alteration need not be limited to the subject, verb, or complement: it may be extended to modifying words, phrases, or clauses. Some judgment is necessary here, as by no means all the arrangements that are physically possible would make sense. The foregoing example is repeated below in the inverted form, which sharpens and emphasizes the meaning.

Inverted: The key concept of modern industrial processing is automation.

A slightly more complicated case involving a compound subject and a less common copulative verb is as follows:

Normal: Computer technology and nuclear fission may be considered to be the most important scientific developments of the twentieth century.

Inverted: The most important scientific developments of the twentieth century may be considered to be computer technology and nuclear fission.

One reason why inverted order is often more emphatic than normal (especially with a copulative verb) is that it keeps the reader waiting until the very last word to get the sense of the sentence. Thus a feeling of suspense and climax is introduced. This so-called *periodic* style has been used for centuries by great writers, orators, and historians. Like all good things, it can be overdone; but when used with discretion, it is unquestionably effective. Here is a complex sentence:

Normal: The structure of some proteins is so complex that their synthesis has not yet been achieved.

Inverted: So complex is the structure of some proteins that their synthesis has not yet been achieved.

It is essential to grasp the idea that, though there may be several ways of stating the same fact, not all of them are equally vigorous. Thus it should be the object of a report writer to select from several possible constructions the one that best drives home his point. It is foolish to take the attitude that this is all very well for poets and novelists, but has no importance in technical writing, which is almost wholly expository. On the contrary, it is hard to think of any technique that is more necessary for accurate and forceful scientific exposition.

In this sort of work more can be learned by observing and experimenting than by reading any amount of advice on how to write, much as laboratory work is the best road toward mastery of a science.

In the following sentences which order is clearer and more emphatic? Which gets the point over better?

> *Normal:* Production went up as a result of the new rule.
> *Inverted:* As a result of the new rule, up went production.
> *Normal:* The difficulties of analysis were never so great.
> *Inverted:* Never were the difficulties of analysis so great.

It may sound like double talk to point out, on the heels of extolling the virtues of inverted order, that sometimes normal order is preferable. But it often is. Certainly nothing could improve the effectiveness of Perry's, "We have met the enemy and they are ours," or Henry's, "Give me liberty or give me death!" The only way to decide which order is better in a given case is to try to change it. If normal order gives the most effective results, by all means use it.

It is good practice to write out several variations of a sentence and try to decide among them on the basis of what might be called *impact strength.* For example, in the following sentences one idea is expressed in three different ways—all of them using normal order. They are given in descending order of impact strength.

> Nothing is more informative than a test that duplicates conditions of actual service.
> The most informative test is that which duplicates actual service conditions.
> Duplication of actual service conditions provides a most informative test.

Subordination of Ideas

It may be useful to think of *compound* sentences as represented by a *rectangle* and of *complex* sentences as represented by a *triangle.* The former type, consisting of a number of simple sentences connected by conjunctions, is just as inherently weak as the rectangle from the viewpoint of mechanical structure. A complex sentence, which contains subordinate clauses, is much stronger, as is the triangle, in which the three sides mutually support one another. One way to make reports effective is to throw important points into relief by making them the backbone of the statement and expressing less important points as subordinate elements. Nothing is more tiresome and less specific than a sentence such as:

> We attached the connections and turned on the power and then waited to see how soon the machine would start, but ac current was not available and the tryout had to be postponed.

This sentence contains five coordinate clauses and one subordinate clause. Rickety writing of this nature can be made quite acceptable by creating a few more subordinate elements:

> After attaching the connections and turning on the power, we waited to see how soon the machine would start; but as ac current was not available, the tryout had to be postponed.

Here the main coordinate clauses are *we waited* and *tryout ... postponed;* the other ideas are dropped into secondary, but reinforcing, positions.

Changes of Structure

Not only as a matter of emphasis, but to avoid confusion of meaning, care should be taken to position phrases correctly. The sentences below show what can happen if phrases are carelessly located.

> I have sought evidence in publications of the society which would indicate activities by the society directed toward obtaining acceptance of physics as a profession without much success. (Phrase *without much success* should be changed to *unsuccessfully* and placed after *have.*)
> Several cases of jaundice have been reported, accompanied by mild anemia. (Participial phrase should follow *jaundice.*)

Sometimes more forceful expressions are gained by avoiding the normal position. Generally speaking, the unusual is more striking than the usual; but the greatest care must be taken to determine the difference between thoughtless disregard of structure and intentional changes made for the purpose of emphasis. In the statement,

"In union there is strength," much is gained in force by placing the phrase *in union* first rather than using the weak-kneed normal position, "There is strength in union." Or again, "In the beginning God created the heavens and the earth" is incomparably stronger than, "God created the heavens and the earth in the beginning."

A succession of prepositional phrases is invariably weak. Here is a typical sentence containing no less than six of them:

> The samples remained in the oven for a long period of time without evidence of deterioration of their quality.

In such cases it is advisable to eliminate unnecessary phrases, either entirely or by converting them to other forms:

> The samples remained in the oven for a long time without evident deterioration.

Another example, from a chemistry textbook, shows how poor placement of a critical phrase impairs clarity:

> Early explanations attributed the remarkable changes in chemical activity effected by mere contact with certain substances to a force unique to those substances.

The last seven words in this last sentence are so far from the verb, *attributed,* that the effect is ruined; too many ideas are introduced between *attributed* and *to* for the mind to carry without effort. This obscures the meaning to the point that rereading is necessary. What can be done in such a case? It is clearly undesirable to place the last seven words directly after *attributed.* But this can be done very nicely if the voice of the verb is shifted from active to passive; the object, *changes,* then becomes the subject. The only other change necessary is to drop the useless word *explanations.* The revamped and much more intelligible sentence now reads:

> The remarkable changes in chemical activity effected by mere contact with certain substances were early attributed to a force unique to those substances.

It is a commonplace maxim of grammar texts—one that is as often wrong as hoary rules about splitting infinitives and ending a sentence with a preposition—that the passive voice should be avoided because it is weaker than the active. Intrinsically it is; but often this change permits a desirable shift of emphasis. If the agent, or actor, is more important than the action itself, the passive voice is preferable.

> *Active:* Newton discovered gravitation.
> *Passive:* Gravitation was discovered by Newton.
> *Active:* A man who knew little about the work wrote the report.
> *Passive:* The report was written by a man who knew little about the work.

The decision between two possible constructions often depends on just what it is the author wants to emphasize. The first sentence above is a perfectly good statement about Newton; but if the context at that point happened to concern an argument about who discovered gravitation, the passive version is much better, since it throws the spotlight on the *actor* rather than the *action*.

Some authors believe that the use of the passive voice makes their writing more scientific and more objective, particularly when they are writing about reproducible experiments. Some also consider that the use of *I* or *we* is immodest.

We believe that the first personal pronoun is not necessarily a sign of immodesty or subjectivity, and that sometimes considerations of objectivity and responsibility, no less than of style, demand its use. Careful avoidance of it is certainly no guarantee of virtue. For example, it is not uncommon to read such self-references as:

> Extraction of this enzyme is difficult, but after long refluxing, it was decided by this author to. . . .

It is inaccurate to pretend in writing that beliefs are held and assumptions made without contamination by human fallibility. "It is assumed" or "It is believed" may be fine for reminding a reader of customarily understood beliefs and assumptions, but it is only fair to the reader to let him know when these beliefs and assumptions are original, and the simplest way is just to say, "I have assumed. . . ."

There are numerous other changes in structure that can aid forceful composition and help to make meaning more specific. A few of these are summarized:

(1) Change noun to phrase

Weak: Clark was given the responsibility of record keeping.
Strong: The responsibility of record keeping was given to Clark.

(2) Change adjective to phrase

Weak: The motor was installed on a 316-steel foundation.
Strong: The motor was installed on a foundation of 316 steel.
Weak: He was a high-principled man.
Strong: He was a man of high principles.

(3) Change verb to permit inverted order

Weak: Rubber-based paints have the advantage of faster drying properties over oil-based paints.
Strong: The advantage of rubber-based paints over oil-based paints is their faster drying properties.
Best: Rubber-based paints dry faster than oil-based. (An active form here shows action; there are many occasions when this form is best. Note, however, that the sense has been slightly changed.)

(4) Omit needless relative pronouns

Weak: The results which they obtained did not check with the experiments which had been carried out in the pilot plant.
Strong: The results they obtained did not check with the experiments carried out in the pilot plant.

(5) Avoid questionable innovations

In recent years there has been a tendency to use a string of nouns and adjectives to modify a single noun (Pentagon style), and to convert nouns and adjectives into verbs at random (Madison Avenue style). The only real objection to such practices is that they often make hash out of an important communicative effect and add nothing of value. The important considerations are emphasis, directness, and clarity—not puristic devotion to rules.

If these objectives can be gained by some innovation of style, by all means use it; otherwise avoid it by an appropriate change of structure. Here are some examples:

Pentagon: A good thing to do when a *buried tank flammable liquid storage facility* is being planned is to discuss the plans with local building groups.
Better: A good thing to do when planning to install buried tanks for storing flammable liquids is to discuss the plans with local building groups.
Madison Avenue: After *contacting* our client, we *finalized* the contract.

Better: After discussion with our client, we signed the contract.
Madison Avenue: The employees opted for a longer coffee break.
Better: The employees chose (or voted for) a longer coffee break.

Also avoid such weak and stereotyped expressions as *facility, manufacturing units, oftentimes, period of time, think in terms of, due to the fact that,* etc. Make every word say something specific. This is known as the "economy" of style.

Placement of Adverbs

Usually an adverb follows the verb it modifies, but often it is more emphatic when placed elsewhere, especially at the beginning or end of the sentence or clause (as is done in this sentence with *usually* and *often*). If you want to call attention to a word, place it where it would not naturally occur, provided that this does not disrupt the structure or otherwise confuse the meaning. For example, it is better to say, "The ships could have passed safely" than "The ships could safely have passed." The latter is weak because it not only makes an awkward split of the verb phrase *could have passed* but also buries the emphatic word *safely* in the middle of the sentence.

It is almost invariably weak to place two *-ly* adverbs side by side; find another place for one of them.

The press operated slowly immediately after being repaired.

Here an improvement can be made by starting the sentence with the phrase *immediately . . . repaired,* or by substituting for *immediately* some other adverb like *just* or *right.*

Some newspapers have a "house" rule which requires placing all adverbs *before* a verb or verb phrase. Thus one usually reads something like, "This always is done," instead of the more normal "This is always done."

One reason for this rule may be a dislike of splitting a verb phrase. But there is nothing inherently wrong or weak about this practice; it is just another case of "sometimes you do and sometimes you don't." Lincoln didn't hesitate to say: ". . . have thus far so nobly advanced," in which the verb phrase *have advanced* is split by no less than four words. Here are some examples of when and when not to divide verb phrases:

> *Good:* I could hardly have seen him sooner.
> *Poor:* I hardly could have seen him sooner.

Here it is obviously essential to split the phrase *could have seen* with the adverb, for the second sentence makes no sense, nor would any other position of the adverb. On the other hand, the choice is not so obvious in the next instance—it must depend on the emphasis desired:

> These samples would *certainly* have passed inspection.
> These samples certainly *would* have passed inspection.

In still other cases it is clearly weak to split the phrase:

> *Poor:* He had unfortunately lost the confidence of the management.
> *Good:* Unfortunately, he had lost the confidence of the management.
> *Poor:* I would in any case have spoken.
> *Good:* I would have spoken in any case.

Repetition

The effectiveness that can be gained by repeating words or phrases is often overlooked in the effort to comply with misunderstood or imaginary rules. It is true that careless reuse of a word can be annoying, and that it often impairs the impact of a sentence or paragraph. Such cases can usually be taken care of by substituting pronouns for nouns, or by varying the selection of adjectives. Watch out for such inadvertencies as:

> The cause of the trouble with the tube was the fact that the lining of the tube was faulty.
> Technical personnel are hard to find today because technical graduates are few and technical training is expensive.

In expository writing, repetition is desirable more often than not, to avoid any possibility of mistaken reference:

> Evolution of hydrogen is dangerous because hydrogen is highly flammable.

If there is a question as to whether or not to repeat a word, the chances are that it should be repeated (as is done in this sentence).

For securing emphasis, repetition is one of the most effective devices in a writer's bag of tricks. Intelligently used, it can add tremendous punch to technical communication. A recent trade journal article affords an interesting example. What would happen to the effect the author wishes to convey if the structure were changed to eliminate repetition?

> This is the *paper* industry as it exists today, and you will see that there are very wide differences of products running all the way from the General Motors Annual Report printed in four colors, to butter cartons, to a roofing *paper*, to a facial tissue. But all these products are *paper* in one form or another. They are all *paper* products. They are all the *paper* industry.

For all its informality, this is an excellent paragraph, and you will note at the end repetition not only of a word but of almost an entire sentence. This is topnotch communication. It is remarkably similar to a definition of government written over fifty years ago by John Fiske:

> *Government*, then, is the directing or managing of such affairs as concern all the people alike ... *Government* is something which is supported by the people and *kept alive* by taxation. There is no other way of *keeping it alive*.

Repetition of this type should be cultivated rather than avoided. The Gettysburg Address furnishes excellent examples of repetition deliberately used for effectiveness. Though less than 250 words long, it contains the following repeated words: *nation,* 5 times; *here,* 7 times; *we,* 10 times; *dedicate,* 6 times.

This is not to say that careless and slovenly repetition is permissible. Whether repetition is deliberate or accidental can best be determined by reading your work aloud or, better yet, by having somebody read it to you. Rarely is this done by inexperienced writers, but there is no better way to catch annoying repetitions and evaluate general effectiveness. Here are several other instances of effective repetition quoted from great literature:

> But in a larger sense, *we cannot* dedicate, *we cannot* consecrate, *we cannot* hallow this ground.

Judge not, that ye be not judged, for with whatsoever judgment ye judge
ye shall be judged.
For Brutus is an *honorable man;* so are they *all, all honorable men.*
All hail, Macbeth and Banquo; Banquo and Macbeth, all hail!

Parallel Construction

Part of the purpose of this chapter is to discourage blind adherence to rules and to encourage independent choice of style based
on clearness and correct emphasis. However, in the case of parallel
construction, its unvarying necessity needs to be stressed. There is
hardly an instance where deviating from it would add to the clarity
of the statement. This indeed is the only valid criterion of any
rule of style. To present a sequence of ideas in a series of clauses
or phrases, decide on what structure to use and apply it consistently
to the entire series. The idea of parallel construction is indicated
below:

Correct: Main clause
                          subordinate clause
                          subordinate clause
                          subordinate clause

or

                 Main clause
                          infinitive, gerund, or participle
                          infinitive, gerund, or participle
                          infinitive, gerund, or participle

Wrong: Main clause
                          subordinate clause
                          infinitive
                          participle
                          gerund

Once the construction is established, it should be rigidly adhered
to. Often, but not always, it can be a matter of voluntary choice,
but once the decision has been made, every care should be exercised
not to violate the parallelism. Obviously certain verbs require use
of an infinitive, others take *that* clauses, still others gerunds or participles. A few may be used with one construction or another. This

is commonly true of verbs indicating indirect discourse (*say, tell, think, believe, know, consider,* and the like). It is equally correct to say, "I knew him to be honest" and "I knew that he was honest"; but it would be undesirable to say, "I knew him to be honest and that he would make an excellent employee." Because of the inherent awkwardness of infinitive constructions after such verbs, it is preferable to use two *that* clauses in such cases.

The principle of parallelism applies not only to subordinate constructions but to main (or coordinate) clauses as well. Indeed, it applies to all structures that can be used in sequence, including sentences within a paragraph. There are few style weaknesses more common than disregard of parallel construction, and any writer will do well to become aware of its importance.

The following unhappy sentence is typical of many technical reports:

> The requirements of a good paint are that it give a uniform coating; to be water and corrosion-resistant; and ease of application.

There are three different constructions after the main verb (*are*): (1) a subordinate clause introduced by *that,* (2) an infinitive phrase, and (3) a noun. Such mixtures are not only a breach of accepted principles of good writing, but—even more important— they are hard to follow and ineffective. This sentence might be reconstructed in two ways; it makes little difference which is selected as long as parallel structure is maintained:

> The requirements of a good paint are that it give uniform coating; that it be water and corrosion-resistant; and that it be easy to apply. (All clauses— disregard repetition of *that it*.)
>
> The requirements of a good paint are production of a uniform coating; water and corrosion resistance; and ease of application. (All nouns.)

The writer must make minor changes of wording as well as of construction whenever the sense demands them; if they cause any difficulty, there is probably something wrong with the facts expressed by the sentence.

Here are a couple of shorter examples, cited to show the tremendous contrast in effectiveness between parallel and mixed constructions.

1. I came; I was an observer; I defeated the enemy.
   I came, I saw, I conquered.
2. Victory or die!
   Victory or death!

In the first example, there are three coordinate clauses, each with a different type of verb; in the second, two nouns are preferable to a noun and a verb. Such instances could be multiplied indefinitely. For examples of correct parallelism examine these:

The public needs less to be informed than to be reminded.
Our fathers brought forth on this continent a new nation, conceived in liberty, and dedicated to the proposition that all men are created equal.

Beginning and End

The beginning and the end—especially the end—are the most emphatic locations in a sentence or a coordinate clause. Many of the changes in structure and position of sentence elements discussed previously (especially inverted order) owe their effectiveness to the fact that they transfer the most significant words or phrases to either the first or last position. If normal order would require a word or phrase at the end, emphasis may be gained by moving it to the beginning, and vice versa. It is for this reason that "Slowly he closed the file" is more forceful than "He closed the file slowly," "In union there is strength" than "There is strength in union." Compare the following sentences and note the sacrifice in emphasis when the climactic word *victories* is relegated to the middle of the sentence:

Whether in chains or in laurels, liberty knows nothing but victories.
Liberty knows nothing but victories, whether in chains or in laurels.

This is a good example of a sentence in which normal order is by far the best; the most important thing of all is to get your *impact* words either first or last.

Corollary to this beginning-ending emphasis is the location of less important elements at or near the middle. In general, the principle of strong-weak, weak-strong is to be recommended wherever special effectiveness is desired; but as usual, there are many exceptions to this, and each case must be decided on its merits. Here are some examples (emphatic words are italicized):

> *The first requirement* of a successful project is a sound and workable *plan*.
> *To be successful,* an idea must be not only conceived, but experimentally *developed*.
> *First* in importance we place the category of *aliphatics*.

Why should the end necessarily be the strongest position? One reason is that it represents the natural top of the climax. By arranging the structure of a sentence so that the meaning is not apparent until the very last word or words, a writer can suspend attention and focus it on the most important point. This is the periodic style previously referred to. In the second sentence above, it would be weak to place the infinitive phrase at the end, partly because the most emphatic word, *developed,* would then be too near the middle, and partly because this would result in an awkward pause, followed by an anticlimactic afterthought as follows:

> An idea must be not only conceived, but experimentally developed, to be successful.

The fact that the word *successful* is indeed important, and yet is clearly undesirable at the end, is still another instance of how impossible it is to make any invariable rules about word order.

The point may be illustrated further with several longer samples showing the effectiveness to be achieved by attention to the beginning and the end.

> *Good:* If the experiments are successful and the company decides to enter the equipment business, it is the responsibility of the committee to point out that such a venture would involve a large capital outlay.
> *Poor:* If the experiments are successful and the company decides to enter the equipment business, large capital outlay will be necessary and the committee feels responsible for pointing this out.
> *Good:* The efficiency of the conveyor system was found to be unexpectedly low, with the result that continuous delivery of raw materials to the machines has been seriously impaired.
> *Poor:* There was found to be unexpectedly low efficiency of the conveyor system, which has resulted in serious interruption of raw material delivery to the machines.

The only way to attain a degree of mastery of forceful style is to be alive to its importance, to study other reports and journal articles with the principles of effective word order in mind, and to revise whatever you write with special care. When you read, try to see how often your train of thought is abruptly derailed by hodge-podge sentences. You find them in newspapers, technical journals, and popular magazines, though almost never in the *Scientific American,* which can be recommended as a model for technical exposition.

Sentences

Recently there has been much ado about the average number of words per sentence, the average number of syllables per word, fog indexes, and other such mechanical criteria. There is unquestionably some value in realizing that sentences can often be too long for easy comprehension, or too short for pleasing and effective style. However, there is no reason why a writer should need a computing machine at his elbow for the purpose of compiling a statistical survey of the word and syllable content of his report; nor is there any mysterious virtue in having sentences average some predetermined number of words.

If the points discussed in this chapter are studied and put into practice, much of the indefiniteness and scrambling of sense which are likely to occur in long sentences will disappear automatically: properly balanced sentence elements, parallel structure, emphatic word order, and correct positioning of adverbs and phrases will give the results desired. Long sentences have legitimate uses and can be effective in the hands of a careful writer.

It is entirely possible to have vigorously written, logically balanced prose in which some sentences may exceed fifty words in length.

It is good general practice to stick to reasonably short sentences, avoiding especially the tendency to write long compound sentences loosely threaded together with conjunctions. The whole point of the discussion of sentence length really revolves around considerations of effectiveness, clarity, and force. A poorly organized short sentence can be more misleading and ambiguous than a well-organized long one.

In technical report writing nothing will replace meticulous attention to specific accuracy of meaning and dynamic word order. These require practice and diligent revision.

Figures of Speech

Figures of speech are nothing more than tricks of meaning or word order deliberately used to heighten the effect of a given thought or statement. Some are so commonplace that one uses them unconsciously. The writing of novelists and poets is liberally sprinkled with them, and to a smaller extent they are useful in ordinary descriptive and expository prose, either to supply a light and semi-humorous touch or to point up a dull sentence or paragraph. Admittedly, they are often based on imaginative and emotional factors that are the very things technical reports are supposed to steer clear of. The text of this book contains several of these figures; for the interest of the reader, we shall list and comment on these, at the same time assuring him that there are many others.

Name of Figure	Definition	Example
Litotes	Affirming something by denying its opposite	"The results were not good."
Personification	Describing an inanimate thing as if it were a person	"This *unhappy* sentence" (page 152, line 14)
Simile	Comparison (stated)	"Words are regarded as plastic materials, not prefabricated units" (page 136, line 7)
Metaphor	Comparison (implied)	"lights and shadows of emphasis" (page 135, line 12) "boilerplate prose" (page 136, line 9) "rickety writing" (page 144, line 11)
Anaphora	Intentional repetition for effect	See page 150 (example on paper industry)

CHAPTER 11 *Definitions and Multiple Meanings*

G. G. HAWLEY

Executive Editor, Reinhold Book Division

If all words had single-valued meanings there would be no trouble in choosing the right word—but language would be flat and colorless. Since the human mind has many of the qualities of an integrating machine, and can recognize relationships among separate concepts and organize them into new thought structures, it is natural that language is full of multiple definitions.

After an author has written a report, has organized it logically, has properly discriminated by using words that mean what he wishes to say, has used strong and specific words and varied sentence lengths, and has followed all the advice he gleaned from countless sources, he ought to go back and read his report thoroughly—aloud.

He may find that he cannot distinguish between a verb and a noun such as in this classified ad found in a Canadian paper: "Unmarried girls to pack fresh fruit and produce at night."

The author may become aware that some words mean one thing to a scientist and another to a musician, for example, the word *resonance*. Unless the context completely clarifies the intended meaning, a reader may think the word *conductivity* refers to electricity, when the author intended it to refer to heat transfer.

The previous experience of a reader will determine the interpretation of a word. An engineer engaged in development projects will think of *technical reports* as interim progress reports or terminal reports. A product engineer will think of a routine listing of production and quality control data. A sales engineer will think of an analysis of industrial markets. To a design engineer a description of a new piece of equipment will be a technical report. A consulting engineer will think of a detailed problem analysis with recommendations. A basic researcher will think of a survey of the literature on a given problem or a report of a fundamental laboratory investigation. The expression "technical report" used in this book refers to all these various types of reporting.

Exact Definitions

Adults attach importance to the names of things and ideas in their environment. What we are familiar with, what we can name, we seem to understand. Anthropologists say that man's belief in the potency of names was one of the earliest human traditions. As a new activity achieves maturity, it also attains a nomenclature. Systematically, every component is named. In order for a technician, an engineer, or a scientist to understand a mechanism, he usually must know the nomenclature of its various parts.

In knowing or understanding an instrument, species, or concept, more is involved than just the ability to name it or to list its parts. One must be able to relate essentially similar classes of devices, species, or concepts, and to describe the significant, identifying characteristics which differentiate each individual from other members of its group. The report author must be certain that his terms are not subject to misinterpretation, and he must realize the importance of defining his terms.

A definition is an explanation or limitation of an object or idea that distinguishes it from all other objects or ideas. Definition is basic to understanding.

Definitions are verbal maps which indicate or explain what is included within a term and what is excluded. The latter is often communicated by implication.

A summary of the general principles of definition was given by H. M. Weisman in his paper, "Definition—A Special Expository

Technique in Technical Writing," (*Proc. 1961 Inst. Tech. Ind. Commun.*, Colorado State University, Fort Collins, Colorado, 1961, p. 60.)

(1) Definitions should include everything that the term means and exclude everything the term does not mean.

(2) Definitions should not include the term to be defined or any variant form of it.

(3) Definitions should include the essential qualities of the term defined.

(4) Definitions of terms in which magnitudes are essential should give the essential quantities involved.

(5) Definitions not measurable by quantities, but which are nevertheless limited or bounded by other terms that are closely related or similar, should include essential similarities and differences of the term defined and the terms bordering it.

(6) When practicable, definitions should be stated in simpler or more familiar language than the term defined.

(7) An expanded definition should employ expository devices, such as examples, contrast, comparison, cause and effect, details, analysis, analogy, history, or other such devices as will promote clarity, meaning and interest. Each expanded definition should contain a logical sentence definition of the term being amplified.

(8) Definitions should not be phrased in obscure or ambiguous language.

(9) Definitions should describe, not praise or condemn, the matter being defined.

"Slanted" Definitions

It is just as easy to mislead people by definitions as it is by statistics. It is entirely possible for a definition to be technically accurate and yet have a misleading and even derogatory connotation. This technique is often employed by partisans and demagogues for propaganda purposes, and it can be extremely effective. Its use is certainly undesirable in a report which is devoted to impartial statements of fact. Here are a few definitions that appear to be entirely factual but that leave the reader with a derogatory impression:

God: a fictitious being who is supposed to look after mankind, but is highly inconsistent in doing so.

Mother: a female animal that has had one or more offspring.

Flag: a rectangular piece of colored bunting or other cheap fabric used as a political designation.

Pipe Organ: a box of whistles.

Which of the foregoing list of principles do these biased defini tions violate?

Proper Meanings

"Polypropylene is a thermoplastic resin, and in this sense its history starts with the first thermoplastics. That material, however, is discussed in the first volume . . ." In this statement, taken directly from a book manuscript, one naturally wonders what material is being referred to—polypropylene, the first thermoplastics, or some other plastic. This confusion will persist until it suddenly dawns on the reader that the word "material" is here used in the sense of "subject matter in general," and does not refer to a substance at all. This type of error is the source of much misunderstanding, and even in cases where the writer's meaning is not obscured, it indicates a lack of imagination and word perception which either grates on the sensibility of the reader or provides him with wholly unintended amusement which diverts his attention from the meaning. The word "material" has many meanings, as will at once be evident from the following list:

Phrase	Sense
(1) material evidence	(1) relevant (legal)
(2) raw material	(2) unprocessed
(3) upholstery material	(3) a textile fabric
(4) material for a report	(4) subject matter
(5) writing materials	(5) implements
(6) material things	(6) not spiritual

It is a careful writer's obligation to be aware of such multiple meanings, and to avoid using them indiscriminately. This requires careful attention and an exactness of thought patterns which should be every scientist's stock in trade. Multiple meanings are rather common in scientific writing. There is no easy or simple way to avoid them. Indeed there are cases where the situation was not clear to the writer even after his attention had been called to it. Thus improvment in this respect demands an imaginative awareness of the possibilities of multiple meanings.

In general, there are two things to avoid. (1) Use of the same word in different senses in the same or closely related sentences. A detailed discussion of this has been given above, and a listing of possibilities comprises the balance of this chapter. Many of these examples are of course synthetic, but a substantial number were taken from actual technical manuscripts. Here is a typical case quoted from an article in a scientific encyclopedia. "This phenomenon is in *effect* a close approximation of the Tyndall *effect*." (2) Not only should the careful writer avoid such slipshod terminology, but he would also do well to ponder the accidental humor involved in using ordinary words which contain the same syllable as a technical term occurring nearby. This unintentional punning can be distracting and may thus interfere with the communication intended. For example, in the sentence, "Our attempt to interpret the absorption band was soon abandoned," the verbal repetition of the syllable *band* sounds as if the author were trying to be funny; the impact of the statement is much greater if "given up" is substituted for "abandoned." Such cases are very frequent (see *bridge, arc, cure, earth* in following list) and the writer must be ever aware of the infinitely odd possibilities that lie hidden in some of our most common words. This constitutes an approach to semantics not usually found in books on the subject. We suggest that for practice the interested reader try compiling a few examples of his own, consulting the dictionary when necessary. The English language is both complex and illogical, and its effective use in technical communication requires a fair degree of sophistication.

Note: In the following list, no distinction has been made between noun, adjective, and verb, since the points being illustrated do not in any way depend upon grammatical syntax.

Activity

Common meaning

(1) The condition or state of being active.

(2) An area of participation, as scientific *activities*.

Specific meaning

(1) The rate or extent of a chemical change initiated by a substance or by surface area. (Magnesium has a greater activity than copper; carbon black has high surface activity).

Avoid: The activity of the sales staff in pushing our surface-active agents has been noteworthy.

Better: Substitute "energy" for "activity."

Arc

Special meaning

(1) A portion of the circumference of a circle.

(2) A sustained electric spark occurring between two electrodes.

Avoid: The arc-lamp is an *archaic* means of illumination.

Better: Substitute "old-fashioned" for "archaic."

Association

Common meanings

(1) A group of people united for a common purpose (American *Association* for the advancement of Science)

(2) A connection, affiliation, or relationship, as an *association* of ideas.

Specific meaning

A type of chemical union similar to polymerization involving only a univalent bond.

Avoid: A lecture on association in chemical compounds was given by Professor X, who has recently become associated with this university.

Better: Substitute "joined the staff of" for "become associated with."

Atmosphere

Common meaning

(1) The air surrounding the earth; (2) the general tone or state of a situation or locality, as *an atmosphere of tension,* or *gloomy atmosphere.*

Specific meaning

The unit weight of the air on the earth's surface, used as a unit of pressure.

Avoid: The samples were tested in a humid atmosphere at a pressure of 2 atmospheres.

Better: The samples were tested at high humidity, etc.

Auxiliary

Common meaning

Helpful, especially in the sense of standby equipment, as *an auxiliary motor.*

Specific meaning

A substance used in the textile industry for any of numerous finishing operations, as *this company sells textile auxiliaries.*

Avoid: In addition to our regular textile auxiliary equipment, we installed an auxiliary loom in the finishing department.

Better: Substitute *extra* for *auxiliary.*

Band

Common meanings

(1) A group of people united by a common purpose, as the rebel band.

(2) A narrow strip, as a band of white paint.

(3) A circular strip of rubber.

(4) A group of musicians.

Specific meaning

(1) Wavelength ranges, as in radio transmission and spectrographic analysis.

Avoid: The attempt to interpret the absorption bands was soon abandoned.

Better: Substitute "given up" or "discontinued" for "abandoned."

Base, Basic

Common meanings

(1) Support or foundation (base of a pedestal).

(2) A station or starting point (base of operations).

Specific meanings

(1) A chemical compound that yields hydroxyl ions in aqueous solution.

(2) A mathematical index (log to the base 10).

Avoid: The theory of acid and *base* formation is one of the *basic* concepts of inorganic chemistry.

Better: Change "basic concepts" to "fundamental concepts."

Bearing

Common meanings

(1) Relevant effect of significance (one event may have a bearing on another).

(2) Behavior or social demeanor (he had an impressive bearing at the meeting).

(3) Carrying.

Specific meaning

Part of a machine.

Avoid: Proper selection of *bearing* alloys has an important *bearing* on their performance.

Better: Proper selection of bearing alloys is an important factor in their performance.

Bit

Common meanings

(1) A small portion.

(2) A metal bar in a horse's mouth.

Special meanings

(1) A drill, as an auger and bit.

(2) A unit of information fed into a computer (derived from *binary* di*git*).

Avoid: We did have a *bit of* difficulty in working out a program for the computer.

Better: Change "bit of" to "little."

Bleed

Common meanings

(1) To emit blood.

(2) To extract money from over a long period, as by blackmail.

Specific meanings

(1) Of a dye, to run or diffuse under heat or atmospheric conditions.

(2) To drain liquid from, as to bleed a pipe line or valve.

(3) In bookmaking, to run illustrations flush to the trim edge of the page.

Avoid: The medical book was full of bleed illustrations.

Blush

Common meaning

To become red in the face from embarrassment, shame, and the like.

Specific meaning

Deposition of condensed moisture from the air on the surface of a paint film due to too rapid evaporation of solvent.

Avoid: The unblushing truth was that the solvents developed in our laboratory actually prolonged the life of the paints tested and tended to reduce sagging and blushing.

Better: Substitute "actual" for "unblushing."

Body

Common meanings

(1) An entire physical organism, as human *body*.

(2) The main portion of something, as the *body* of a report, letter, speech or the like; also an automobile *body*.

Specific meaning

Consistency or texture of a material, as a full-bodied oil or varnish.

Avoid: The quick-drying *body* lacquer had insufficient *body*.

Better: Change "body lacquer" to "car lacquer."

Bond

Common meanings

(1) A spiritual unifying bond, as a *bond* of sympathy.

(2) Fetters, as the prisoner burst his *bonds*.

(3) A financial obligation or protection, i.e. government bonds, bonded liquors.

Specific meanings

(1) The strength of adhesion between two surfaces, as a strong *bond* was formed by the adhesive.

(2) The force existing between two or more atoms in a chemical compound.

(3) A kind of writing paper.

Avoid: The company had to issue bonds to obtain sufficient capital to put its new line of permanent-bond cements on the market.

Better: Change "permanent-bond" to "permanent-adhesion."

Bridge

Common meanings

(1) A structure built over a river or depression.

(2) A card game.

Specific meanings

(1) A denture

(2) A device for uniting two electrical circuits.

(3) Part of the nose.

(4) A chemical union of two molecules by means of a shared atom, as an oxygen bridge.

Avoid: Desirable as it seemed to *abridge* the chapter, we felt that it was essential to include some reference to chemical *bridges*.

Better: Substitute "shorten" for "abridge."

Brush

Common meanings

(1) An instrument for cleaning.

　　(2) A slight conflict, as a *brush* with the law.

　　(3) Undergrowth or low bushes.

　　(4) With *up*, to review a subject quickly.

Specific meaning

　　(1) A contact made of carbon or other conductor used in electrical generators.

Avoid: The students decided to *brush up* on their electrical engineering.

Conduct

Common meanings

　　(1) Behavior.

　　(2) To lead a group effort.

　　(3) To carry out, as to conduct an experiment.

Specific meaning

　　To transfer heat or electric current from one point to another through a substance.

Avoid: He *conducted* an experiment in which graphite was used as *conductor*.

Better: He carried out an experiment, etc.

Carrier

Common meaning

　　A bearer or messenger, as a letter carrier.

Specific meanings

　　(1) A bearer of disease germs.

　　(2) A transportation system or company.

　　(3) A kind of pigeon.

　　(4) A conveyor belt or similar device.

　　(5) An inert substance used to support a catalyst in a reaction bed or tower.

Avoid: Extensive work was *carried out* on the best method of selecting an ideal *carrier* for the catalyst.

Better: Change "carried out" to "done" or "performed."

Chalk

Common meaning

　　(1) A soft limestone used for writing on blackboards or the like.

Specific meaning

　　(1) Appearance of filler or similar ingredient on the surface of the product due to minute cracks, usually induced by sunlight or weather.

Avoid: The developments of a series of organic non-chalking pigments chalks up another "first" for the research development.

Better: Substitute "scores" for "chalks up."

Composition

Common meanings

(1) The substances of which a product or material consists, i.e., the composition of clay is aluminum, silicon, and oxygen.

(2) A literary, musical or artistic work.

Specific meanings

(1) Setting up of type for printing.

(2) Proper arrangement of subject matter in a painting.

Avoid: The composition of steel slags was the chief subject matter of the composition.

Converter

Common meaning

(1) One who or that which converts or changes, especially in a religious sense.

Specific meanings:

(1) A fabricator of paper products.

(2) A Bessemer converter used in steel making.

Avoid: It is possible to convert waste paper into usable material.

Better: It is possible to reclaim waste paper.

Crack

Common meanings

(1) A sharp, loud sound, as the *crack* of a whip.

(2) A surface split.

Specific meanings

(1) Purposeful decomposition and rearrangement of molecules, as in petroleum refining.

(2) Disintegration of used tires by a machine designed for this purpose.

Avoid: The surface of the hose used to convey the *cracked* product showed a large number of *cracks* after a week of use.

Better: Substitute "gasoline" for "cracked product."

Cure

Common meaning

(1) To heal, as a disease.

Specific meanings

(1) To preserve by treating with heat or chemicals (ham is cured by smoking).

(2) To alter chemical structure by heat and chemicals; to vulcanize.

Avoid: It was difficult to *procure* a satisfactory *curing* agent.

Better: Change "procure" to "obtain."

Current

Common meanings

   (1) Passing from hand to hand, as paper money.
   (2) Generally accepted, as the *current* meaning.
   (3) Belonging to the present time, as the *current* month.

Specific meaning

   Flowing or running, as of water or electricity.
Avoid: Electric power production is *currently* at its peak.
Better: Change "currently" to "now."

Digestion

Specific meanings

   (1) Chemical breakdown and combustion of nutrition substances in the stomach and intestines.
   (2) An industrial chemical process in which a raw material, such as wood, is reacted with sulfuric acid to form pulp.
Avoid: The report contained a *digest* of the most recent patents on hardwood *digestion*.
Better: Substitute "resume" or "summary" for "digest."

Doctor

Common meanings

   (1) A physician.
   (2) The holder of an advanced degree.
   (3) To adjust the quality of adulterate.

Specific meanings

   (1) A test for sulfur content of petroleum products.
   (2) A knife or blade for removing film from a metal roller.
Avoid: The mixture was doctored up with so much solvent that a doctor knife was required at the take-off.
Better: So much solvent was *added* to the mixture that, etc.

Draw

Common meanings

   (1) To make a line, as for a design or chart.
   (2) To attract the attention of, as the show drew a good crowd.
   (3) To pull out or extract, as a tooth.
   (4) To reason by induction, i.e., draw a conclusion.
   (5) To pull by dragging, i.e., to draw a wagon.

Specific meanings

   (1) To require a certain depth of water, i.e., the ship draws six feet.
   (2) To remove viscera from.

(3) To process a metal rod by pulling it through dies of decreasing size, as to draw wire.

(4) To receive money for services, i.e., to draw a salary.

(5) In games, a tie.

Avoid: May I draw your attention to this drawing of a machine for making cold-drawn wire?

Better: Here is a diagram of a machine for making cold-drawn wire.

Drill

Common meanings

(1) To bore a hole, or an instrument for so doing.

(2) To train by exercise or practice.

Specific meanings

(1) To sow seeds in a furrow.

(2) A fabric of characteristic diagonal weave.

Avoid: A series of tests, or drills, was planned, to familiarize the crew with the quick assembly and operation of drilling rigs.

Dry

General meaning

(1) Absence of moisture, or solvent; hence a machine for removing water from a product is called a *dryer*.

Specific meanings

(1) No consumption of alcoholic beverages.

(2) Uninteresting.

(3) Hardened by polymerization or oxidation, as of certain types of vegetable oils.

(4) Not sweet.

Avoid: The drying of an exterior paint film is promoted by high temperature and dry atmospheric conditions.

Better: Substitute "low humidity" for "dry atmospheric conditions."

Earth

Common meanings

(1) This planet.

(2) Soil or dryland, as distinguished from rocks and ocean.

Specific meanings

(1) Specific groups of metallic oxides, such as rare earths, or alkaline earths.

Avoid: We succeeded in unearthing published data on the rare earths.

Better: Substitute "finding" for "unearthing."

Effect

Common meanings

(1) The result of a cause.

(2) To bring about, as to effect a change.

(3) An over-all impression, as a startling effect.

(4) State of being operative, as the rule goes into effect soon.

Specific meanings

(1) In physics, a phenomenon usually named after its observer or dis-coverer, as the Tyndall effect.

(2) Heat obtained by steam condensation, as a triple-effect evaporator.

Avoid: The matrix effect is, in effect, bypassed.

Better: Replace "in effect" with "actually."

Essential

Common meanings

(1) Indispensable.

(2) Relating to essence or basic existence, as essential art.

Specific meaning

(1) An oil occurring in plants and removed by distillation.

Avoid: The study of perfumes is essentially concerned with essential oils.

Better: Substitute "chiefly" or "primarily" for "essentially."

Evolution

Common meanings

(1) The biological theory of the development of man from higher animals.

(2) The development or working out, as of a plot or plan.

Specific meanings

(1) Emission of a gas from a chemical reaction.

(2) In mathematics, to raise a quantity to a power.

Avoid: Evolution was a theory evolved by Darwin.

Better: Replace "evolve" with "developed" or "presented."

Extract

Common meanings

(1) To draw out or remove physically or by solvent action, as an acetone extract.

(2) A selected portion of a written work.

Specific meanings

(1) The total solids obtained by evaporation.

(2) A concentrate, such as liver extract.

Avoid: Extract steam from the bottom of the extractor.

Better: Remove steam, etc.

Fast

Common meanings
   (1) Rapid in time or motion.
   (2) To abstain from food.
   (3) Dissipated or immoral.

Specific meanings
   (1) Stable, firm, unchanging, as a fast dye.
   (2) Resistant to a toxic substance, as arsenic-fast bacteria.

Avoid: Organic dyes are well suited for fast processing of textiles.
Better: Substitute "rapid" for "fast."

Filler

Common meaning
   (1) One who or that which fills, *e.g.*, a dentist is a filler of teeth.

Specific meanings
   (1) A cheap, bulky material added to a mixture primarily to reduce its cost.
   (2) In a textile fabric the light thread running transversely through the warp.
   (3) A composition used to mend crevices and holes in a surface to be painted.

Avoid: The use of moist *filler* compound caused the wood to *warp*.

Note: "Warp" and "filler" are textile terms and should not be used in other senses in the same sentence. Here, the best solution is to say "filling" instead of "filler."

Fine

Common meanings
   (1) Excellent, splendid, admirable.
   (2) Composed of very small particles or lines, as fine sand, fine print.
   (3) A financial penalty.

Specific meaning
   (1) A measure of quality of precious metals, as the fineness of gold or silver.

Avoid: Fine-ground metals are used as catalysts in petroleum *refining*.
Better: Metals of small particle size, etc.

Flash

Common meanings
   (1) A quick, bright light, as a lightning flash.
   (2) A sudden idea or emotion, as a flash of inspiration.

Special meanings
(1) Flash point: the temperature at which a vapor-air mixture will ignite.
(2) The overflow from a mold, as of plastic or rubber.
(3) To seal or protect portions of a roof from rain.
(4) Coating of a glass product with a film of glass of different color.
Avoid: To inspect for possible leakage of low flash-point solvents, a flashlight should be used.
Better: Never use an open flame to inspect for possible leakage of low flash-point solvents.

Flat
Common meanings
(1) Free from undulations, roughness, hills, etc.
(2) An apartment.

Specific meanings
(1) Of taste, insipid, without character.
(2) Of paints, non-reflecting, low-gloss.
(3) In music, a symbol indicating a half tone lower than "natural."
Avoid: Flat paints can be effectively used on flat surfaces.
Better: Low-gloss paints, etc.

Flux
Common meaning
(1) An unstable condition or continual change, as the flux of financial affairs.

Specific meanings
(1) A liquid discharge from some part of the body.
(2) A material used to promote fusion of metals.
(3) A flow of energy or energetic particles, i.e., neutron flux, magnetic flux.
Avoid using "flux" in any sentence or context in which "reflux distillation" occurs.

Fusion
Common meanings
(1) Blending or mixing together, as a fusion of ideas.
(2) Melting, as fused salts.

Specific meaning
(1) Formation of an element of higher atomic weight from union of hydrogen nuclei, with evolution of energy.

Avoid: There should be no confusion in the meaning of the terms "fission" and "fusion."

Better: Substitute "misunderstanding" for "confusion."

Ground

Common meanings

(1) The earth's surface; land reserved for a special purpose, as a playground.

(2) Basis of belief or argument.

(3) A product of grinding, as ground meat.

Specific meanings

(1) To connect electricity with the ground, which becomes part of the circuit.

(2) Of a ship, to strike bottom.

Avoid: When air is full of fine-ground particles, an electrical potential will be set up which should be grounded by precipitators.

Better: When air is full of *extremely fine* particles, etc.

Hand

Common meanings

(1) A part of the human body.

(2) Applause.

(3) Penmanship.

(4) The cards held by a player.

(5) An indicator on a clock or gauge.

Specific meanings

(1) A unit of measuring the height of animals.

(2) The feeling of a textile fabric.

(3) A bunch of bananas.

Avoid: Playing cards can be made of textiles having an extremely stiff hand.

Better: Playing cards can be made of extremely stiff textiles.

Hard

Common meanings

(1) Difficult.

(2) Severe, as hard feelings, a hard winter.

(3) Not soft; rigid.

Specific meanings

(1) Of liquors, high alcoholic content.

(2) Of water, having a high percentage of dissolved sulfates or carbonates.

(3) Short wavelength x-rays.

(4) Susceptibility to being scratched by another material, as in Mohs scale.

Avoid: Hard water is not hard to find in rocky localities.

Better: Substitute "difficult" for the second "hard," or "easy" for "not hard."

Indicator

Common meanings

(1) A device, such as a dial and arrow, which shows such variables as time, pressure or temperature.

(2) Any standard of performance, as carloadings are an indicator of business activity.

Specific meaning

(1) A substance which shows by change of color the acidity or alkalinity of a solution.

Avoid: In this case use of the most acidic material was indicated.

Better: Substitute "seemed advisable" for "was indicated."

Induction

Common meaning

(1) The installation of an official in public office.

Specific meanings

(1) Reasoning from particulars to generalities.

(2) Acquisition of an electric or magnetic charge by a body lying in or near an electric or magnetic field.

Avoid: The principle of induced current was discovered by Faraday by the process of inductive reasoning.

Better: Faraday established the principle of induced current by careful evaluation of experimental results.

Liver

Common meanings

(1) One who lives, e.g., a fast-liver.

(2) An organ of the body.

Specific meaning

(1) Of printing inks, to gel or partially polymerize.

Avoid: Although the supervisor allowed 400 pounds of ink to liver, this did not prevent *delivery* of the order.

Long

Common meanings

(1) Extended in time or space; lengthy.

(2) To desire ardently, as to long for home.

Specific meanings

(1) Containing a high percentage of an ingredient, e.g., a long-oil paint.

(2) To have a large amount of stock in, as to be long of motor stocks.

Avoid: There was a short discussion of long-oil varnishes.

Better: Substitute "brief" for "short."

Matter

Common meanings

(1) Any written composition, as reading matter.

(2) An important concern, as what is the matter with you?

(3) Things relating to a definite subject, as financial matters.

Specific meanings

(1) Any physical substance that possesses mass.

(2) A particular kind of material, as coloring matter.

(3) Pus or infectious discharge from a wound.

Avoid: No matter what some may think, it has been proved beyond doubt that there is no real difference between matter and energy.

Better: Regardless of what some, etc.

Normal

Common meanings

(1) Conforming to an average, as normal temperature.

(2) Natural or common.

Specific meanings

(1) Denoting a solution of specified strength.

(2) A hydrocarbon molecule in which no C atom is united with more than two other C atoms.

(3) Perpendicular, as a line drawn normal to a surface.

Avoid: It is normal to use tenth normal iodine as a reagent.

Better: Substitute "usual" for the first "normal."

Offset

Common meaning

(1) To counterbalance, as some expenses were offset by savings.

Specific meanings

(1) A shoot used for propagating a plant.

(2) A bend in a rod or pipe to turn it aside from the line.

(3) To transfer ink from one surface to another by contact, as offset printing.

Avoid: This expense was partially offset by the lower cost of the offset process.

Better: Substitute "compensated" for the first "offset."

Order

Common meanings

(1) A society or brotherhood, as a monastic order.

(2) A command.

(3) Conformity to authority, as law and order.

(4) Regular and systematic arrangement, e.g., order of magnitude.

Specific meanings

(1) A quantity of goods purchased.

(2) A biological classification of animals.

Avoid: Zoologists have set up an orderly arrangement of classifying animals, including such groups as species, class, order, and family.

Better: Omit "orderly."

Organic

Common meanings

(1) Having to do with bodily organs, as an organic disability.

(2) Having systematic arrangement, as an organic whole.

Specific meanings

(1) That branch of chemistry concerned with compounds containing carbon.

(2) A form of artistic creation resulting from intuitive feeling rather than from thought.

(3) Pertaining to living organisms.

Avoid: Organic chemistry is a highly organized body of knowledge.

Better: Substitute "systematic" for "organized."

Precipitate

Common meanings

(1) Headfirst, without thought, as precipitate action.

(2) To bring on as a consequence, as to precipitate an event.

Specific meanings

(1) The solid residue of a reaction product.

(2) To condense and fall as rain or snow.

Avoid: The precipitate was analyzed, and the results, when offered in evidence, precipitated a wholly new development in the trial.

Better: Substitute "caused" or "brought about" for "precipitated."

Proof

Common meanings

(1) Incontestible evidence of a fact or truth.

(2) A sample or trial picture or type impression.

Specific meanings

(1) An index of the alcoholic strength of a mixture, as 90-proof whiskey.

(2) In mathematics an operation for testing the accuracy of a postulate or theorem.

Avoid: The court required proof that the flask had contained alcohol.

Better: The court required evidence, etc.

Well

Common meanings

(1) Healthy, not sick.

(2) Satisfactorily, as a job done well.

(3) A shaft dug or drilled in the ground for oil or water.

(4) Completely, fully, as well out to sea.

Specific meanings

(1) A depression or cavity designed for a specific mechanical function, as an ink well.

(2) An open shaft in a building, as a stair or elevator well.

Avoid: The risk involved in drilling an oil well often does not turn out well.

Better: The risk involved in drilling an oil well is often unrewarded.

CHAPTER 12   *Proper Words in*
Proper Places

"Proper words in proper places make the true definition of style," said Jonathan Swift. Words carry an appropriateness to the subject assigned by the reader and the writer. This principle applies to all phases of an author's use of language, but is easiest to demonstrate in a discussion of words. Obviously the words spring primarily from a need to discuss the subject and must fit the subject. In discussing a machine, its parts have to be named and its functions described, whether in technical or popular terms; in discussing chemistry there are words about compounds and reactions and theories; in discussing the influence of newspapers there are editorials and headlines and leads and propaganda and Associated Press and paid advertising. But there will be a number of words not specifically demanded by the subject, that one writer might use and another not. In these, some balance is to be struck between the reader's expectation and the writer's usual habits of expression.

The basic problem in intelligibility in technical reporting may be divided into three phases:

Semantics, which concerns the communication of ideas by means of words and the maintenance of the reader-writer relationship at a mutual level of understanding.

Synonyms, which have to do with words having similar meanings in all or some of their senses.

Syntax, which involves the accurate expression of ideas by arrangement of words in a sentence according to established usage.

Semantics

The division of linguistics that studies the meaning and changes of meaning of words is called semantics, or semasiology.

Semiology is the all-embracing study of signs and languages, and is divided into three parts:

(1) *Syntactics,* the study of signs and the relation between signs. Syntactics might be considered the traffic rules of language.

(2) *Semantics,* the study of relations between the signs of a language and their referents or meanings.

(3) *Pragmatics,* the study of signs and the relation of their users.

Because of the complexities of language, semantics cannot be entirely divorced from syntactics and pragmatics. Various kinds of ambiguities and vague expressions can be traced to any of these three branches of semiology. Semantics is the most significant branch of this language study for the technical writer. Much of the literature of semantics is theoretical. Engineers and scientists can find some hints in those theories as to how to apply semantic concepts to everyday problems in report writing. In the last few decades this field has been particularly active under the leadership of C. K. Ogden, I. A. Richards, S. I. Hayakawa, Count Alfred Korzybski, and others. These men have added much to our knowledge and understanding of words and the ways in which they are used and misused.

(1) Ogden, E. K. and Richards, I. A., "The Meaning of Meaning," Harcourt, Brace, New York, 1959 (Original ed., 1923).

(2) Chase, S., "The Tyranny of Words," Harcourt, Brace, New York, 1938.

(3) Korzybski, A. B., "Science and Sanity," Science Press, Lancaster, Pa., 1941.

(4) Hayakawa, S. I., "Language in Action," Harcourt, Brace, New York, 1941.

(5) Cherry, Colin, "On Human Communication," Technology Press, Cambridge, Mass., 1957.

(6) Michaelson, H. B., "Semantics in Report Writing," *Technical Writers and Editors Journal,* Summer Issue, 1957.

(7) Fowler, H. W. and Fowler, F. G., "The King's English," 3rd ed., Clarendon Press, London, 1940.

(8) Evans, B. and Evans, C., "A Dictionary of Contemporary American Usage," Random House, New York, 1957.

Denotation. The words the author uses and the words he recognizes get their meaning from the way they have been and are being used by people in speaking and writing. A word means what it stands for to the writer and reader, what in their experience or imagination or feeling it refers to. The object or class of objects, situation, quality, idea, fancy, or act to which a word refers is called its *referent,* and by representing this referent a word gets a core of meaning, its *denotation.*

In Lewis Carroll's "Through the Looking Glass" Humpty Dumpty announces: "When I use a word it means just what I choose it to mean—neither more nor less." "The question is," said Alice, "whether you can make words mean so many different things." "The question is," said Humpty Dumpty, "which is to master— that's all."

Humpty Dumpty is defining by *stipulation.* He attributes to a word or term a specific meaning he wants it to have. Scientists are constantly using stipulative definitions in coining names for matters they discover or assigning new terms or applying an old term in a new way to encompass an activity, process, or object which has evolved from their research. Reports and papers sometimes say, "When the term X is used in this paper, it means thus and such."

The meaning of a word is in the author's head. It is transmitted to his reader only if rapport can be established between the two people. The meaning is not inherent in the word. One way to show that meaning is not in the word is to consider some words that are used in various senses. To take common examples: What is a knot? a cut? a seal? a pump? What do you do when you pump or strike, or fly, or fall? A knot may be a tie in some sort of rope, a group of people, a spot on a board, a tough problem, the measure of a ship's speed. The meaning is not in the word but in what it refers to. What it does refer to is usually clear from the sentence in which it is used, that is from its *context,* from the frame of reference given it by the author. It is so difficult to say how much is understood from a given word and how much from context that it is not very profitable to consider the precise meaning of isolated words.

An author's pride in his first draft may well diminish as he rereads the report for defects. Here is his opportunity for self-criticism and for an appraisal of the flavor of his writing. Many words carry with them an aroma which is headier than their meaning. Such words are highly useful in *moving* a reader, but they are not so successful always in *informing* him. The technical writer cannot permit himself to mix emotion with information, which means that he must be very careful to choose his words for their *denotation,* not their connotation.

Compare the following statements:

(1) Recognizing the sacredness of human rights, the management has begun a promotion policy based on the principle of freedom in equality of opportunity.

(2) Promotion will be issued upon merit.

The first sentence is an example of emotion and feeling, often found in advertising and politics (connotation); the second sentence says the same thing with fewer words and less emotion. This is technical writing, or denotation.

By persistent rereading and rewriting the author will seek out redundancies, connotations, and awkward constructions. By improving the grace and harmony of his literary style he makes his work easier to read. His final reading should be an objective search for the language ambiguities that tend to hamper even the most careful writer's style. Since clarity is inherent in a sound literary style, the science of word meanings has important practical implications.

Definiteness of meaning varies considerably among different words, depending in part on the exactness with which they bring to mind specific referents. Words divided into several classes will show this varying definiteness. Other groups could be made according to some trait of their meaning, but these are enough to suggest that there are different relations between words and what they stand for and that the problem of using words exactly is more complex than it might seem at first.

Concrete Words. First, and most definite and specific, are concrete words whose meaning is established by more or less regular reference to actual objects. *Lab bench,* for example, has a definite core of meaning because it is used to apply to a kind of table. Even though people might disagree over a particular untypical lab bench

—one might be called a *desk* or another a *counter*—almost always the meaning of *lab bench* would be definite enough for a writer's purposes. Soapstone top, oiled wood bench, "Formica" top bench are more definite in their reference. The specific image that a word raises in the minds of different people will vary somewhat, but in each there is a core of meaning out of each person's experience. A word with which a person has had no experience (perhaps *tenon, farthingale, spandrel*) will have little meaning for him.

Relative Words. Relative words name qualities and have a fairly definite core of meaning, or at least a direction of meaning. Their reference in a given instance depends a good deal on the experience and intention of the user.

Red, for instance, may mean angry, it may mean Communist, or it may mean embarrassed. To a person in the "upper brackets," a family with $5,000 a year income might be *poor,* but to a person on relief or welfare that family might be *well off. Pretty red crystals* might mean to one person that the crystals are *almost red,* to another, *quite red,* and to another the crystals would be a *beautiful red.* Similarly, *warm, heavy, thick, rough, honest, beautiful, tall* are relative in meaning. Some attempts have been made to make possible an exact naming of colors in art or in physics, standardized weights and measures, or in definitions by law of words like *drunk* and *speeding* so that they can be used in courts.

In using these descriptive words, especially those that record attitudes and judgments, the most important thing is to remember the various degrees, the exact shading that it is possible to express. In ordinary conversation many distinctions are not made. A person is all *wet,* or a *ham,* or a *brick,* or a *good egg,* or a show is a *flop* or a *wow.* But in writing, especially in technical writing, conveying the precise shade of meaning intended requires the writer to have empathy for the reader. To convey exact meaning is to know the precise effect of the words on the reader. To try this is challenging and is a step toward civilized living—as well as a triumph in the use of words.

Abstract Words. Even more difficult to use accurately are abstract words, which do not have specific referents against which their meaning can be checked. The most definite abstract words refer to acts or relationships or directions: *citizenship, civil rights, cost, differentiation, freedom, ionization, responsibility, valence.*

They have definite meaning simply because English-speaking people generally agree in the way they are used. Other abstract words are collective, that is, they stand for a gathering of individuals—*council, college, music, science.* They summarize one or more common traits belonging to a number of particular people or things or situations and have a pretty definite core of meaning, but may be used with very different values. The real danger in such words is that, often as they are used, one may lose sight of the facts for which they stand.

"The *youth* in science" may actually keep us from seeing the thousands of young people referred to and may let us or lead us to make statements that we never would if we visualized clearly even a dozen of them. *Capital,* for instance, means employers and investors collectively, and *labor* stands for workmen. But as they are ordinarily used, there is no notion of specific people suggested; they may be used as words of praise or blame, so that feeling would be more important than reference to any group of living persons.

Many other words do not have referents even as commonly agreed upon as those. The meaning of such words as *research, art, derivative, evil, education* is a complex reasoning and feeling that varies from person to person. An adequate definition of any such word would be an essay, and its meaning would depend on the past experience, the emotions, and the general outlook of the person making it. Obviously understanding is difficult here, because the listener or reader has had different experience, different feeling, and different philosophy, so that the difficulty is multiplied. Writers should intend to lead a reader not just to words but to consciousness of objects or ideas in a real or imagined world. To help, the author can often give specific, concrete examples of what he means. The fundamental sin is using words that do not "refer to something," do not, that is, have meaning to readers.

Of course, for exact and reasonable communication it is highly important that a writer know where in the range of meaning of abstract words his core of meaning falls and that he make this clear to his readers. Trying to attain fairly exact communication is one reason for the prevailing *concreteness* of modern technical report style.

Connotation. The denotation of a word is (more or less) informative and factual and is what ordinarily is meant by its *meaning;* it is what a dictionary defines it to be. But this meaning is somewhat affected by the circumstances in which the word has been generally used and by the particular context in which it occurs. This suggested quality, as distinct from the central core of meaning, is called its *connotation.*

Looking at a few groups of words having substantially the same denotation will bring out this quality and show why one could not be indiscriminately substituted for another.

childlike (approving)	childish (derogatory)
saliva (factual, slightly formal, with scientific suggestion)	spit (common, but an "ugly" word)
drunk (general use)	intoxicated (more polite)
under the influence (euphemistic, minimizing)	stoned, soused (not quite derogatory, but slangy)
appendectomy (professional)	appendicitis operation (slightly
had his appendix out (colloquial)	formal)

The connotations of these words suggest an attitude or a feeling of the person using them and would arouse a similar (or perhaps an antagonistic) attitude or feeling in most readers. The context in which the word has been generally used, the level of usage it comes from, and the general professional attitude toward its referent and toward the people who generally use it all contribute to these suggested qualities. The value of slang and of much profanity is more in the suggestion of the words than in their denotation. The connotation of these words may change as they or their referents move up or down in professional esteem. *Atom* started as a word of ultimate scientific subdivision but is now limited to chemical subdivision, and is currently a nontechnical word of the political world.

No Meaning. Sometimes a word is used for a meaning that it has not yet acquired in its previous history. Such as:

How are the debaters outwitting their *prototypes* (competitors)?

Usually such errors occur when a writer is attempting a level of usage in which he is not at home or when he confused two words of similar sound (*temerity—timidity; frigidity—fragility; flaunt—flout; climatic—climactic; cartridge—cartilage*).

Confusions in writing of words that sound alike, *homonyms,* are a matter of spelling rather than of meaning. Even if the context makes the meaning clear, as it often does, such inaccuracies are badges of the unlettered or evidence of the unqualified.

> The fourth table summarizes *solvent* (salient) features of the six-batch run.
> The notes are on a printed Multilith mat with *non-reproducible* (non-reproducing) ink.
> The *deliberation* (liberation) of the H₂S gradually increased.
> Telephone *inquisitions* (inquiries) consume a fourth of our day.

The remedy for this sort of error is for the author to stay within his known vocabulary or to check with a dictionary when he is not quite sure of a word.

Too Little Meaning. Sometimes words are used that are too general to convey an exact meaning. They are more characteristic of conversation than of writing. Common words like *fine, bad, good* should usually be replaced by more definite adjectives, and even words like *interesting* or *important* frequently stand for some particular sort of interest or importance that could better be named, so that the reader's thought could be brought nearer to the writer's intention.

Too Much Meaning. Exaggeration is a legitimate form of expression, but often words are too intense for a technical writer's meaning; they carry too much meaning. Perhaps a *most* should be *many,* or a superlative should be reduced to a less extreme statement, or an *only* or *nothing but* should allow for other possibilities. Or extreme words like *unique, intriguing, thrill* should be replaced by words that are merely descriptive. Frequently, an author may recognize exaggerated meaning and compound the error by qualifying the unqualifiable: *half perfect, almost infinite, nearly light-tight.*

The best remedy is to revise the writing and to resolve to present the subject as it really is. A little calm will help a writer express himself in words that describe his ideas.

Synonyms

A synonym is a word of nearly the same meaning as another. Often the real difference between them is in the connotation. There are very few pairs of interchangeable words. Because of these differences in connotation, merely trying to escape repetition of a word is not a sufficient motive for using a synonym.

As a rule, testing the exactness of words is a matter of revision. The author can see then the context in which they are to stand and can test them for precision of meaning, for appropriateness to the subject and to the readers, for their degree of formality or informality. Sometimes he can find a single word to take the place of a long phrase; sometimes he can replace a general or ambiguous word with one of specific meaning, as *hard* might be *rigid, difficult, repellant, unbreakable,* or *tough.* Sometimes the change is to bring a word in line with the level of usage of the rest of the report, choosing one either more or less formal: *want—wish, desire; fast— rapidly.*

Sometimes it is a matter of finding the exact name for something that the writer has seen but has never named in one word, like the small platform on which an orchestra conductor stands (*podium*), or a glass container in which to carry out chemical reactions (*test tube, reactor, beaker, erlenmeyer flask,* or a *florence flask*).

The prime source of synonyms is reading. A person usually has a plentiful and ready supply of words in the fields in which he is really at home. Cultivating a habit of observing and using words found in reading is the best background for making the choice of precise words.

The idea is prevalent among scientists as well as other professional men that simple repetition of a leading word in a sentence or short period constitutes an offense. To them it is *tautology,* or unprofitable repetition of meaning. This false sense of tautology often creates awkward circumlocutions. If the word first accepted is precisely the word wanted, to vary it is to vary the sense, confuse the argument, and vex the reader.

In the sentences below the term first used and farther along replaced by synonyms should have been repeated, as shown in parentheses:

> This species is based upon a single incomplete specimen; a second example (specimen) showing similar sculpture was found in the same place.
>
> Most of the phenomena are due to lack of water rather than to the presence of that agent (water).
>
> Normal hexane and 3-methyl hexane are found in place of the aromatic equivalents (benzene and toluene).

Where the names are explicit, the more abstract generic terms should be replaced.

The phrase *the same* should not be used to represent a preceding noun, as in the following sentence:

> This is not a mere report on reports but a monograph on the same (reports).

The writer of the following sentence avoided what he thought would be tautology not by the use of a synonym but by too much condensation:

> The formation is of fresh-water origin in the west and brackish in the east.

It should read:

> The formation is of fresh-water origin in the west and of brackish-water origin in the east.

The preceding examples show that precision in the use of words is difficult. Words may carry only approximate meanings because human beings are not precise. Complete failure in communication is possible because of careless or unhappy choice of words, and sometimes an author fails to make full use of the facilities of our language. But a sincere effort to convey the author's ideas can succeed.

Extreme precision is also not always desirable. A person who in conversation is overexact or overcareful is likely to become a bore, sacrificing immediate appeal to precision. In simple explanation or statements of fact in technical report writing, the words are likely to be used for their central core of meaning. In attempts to persuade, sell, convince, or any sort of emotional appeal, the connotation counts for more.

Words That Weaken. Most ideas are not particularly complicated or difficult. Simple ideas ought to be presented simply so that they make a direct appeal to the readers. The style in which ideas are expressed is often a handicap and, especially in amateur writing, will make the reading more tiring than the idea requires. Words that may convey meaning but that kill the interest of a reader are a blight on technical reporting.

Trite Words. A *trite expression* is a phrase that is grossly overused. It is similar to a cliché or a hackneyed word. Certain necessary functional words—*a, the, an,* the prepositions, the conjunctions—do not wear out, nor do the actual names of things and acts and qualities with which we have daily familiarity. Expressions that deserve to be called trite are something more than the direct, natural words or phrases. We can call for *bread* as often as we need to, but *staff of life* is quite a different matter. Linguistically it is a metaphor, once bright and perhaps even startling, but now actually threadbare and hardly serving a weak attempt at humor.

Some writers habitually begin sentences with *It is, There is,* or *There are;* this practice not only multiples words, but has the effect of putting the subject nominative in an inferior place instead of at or near the beginning of the sentence; also these have become almost trite expressions.

It is the function of the contact substance to absorb the reacting gases at its surface.

The sentence could be rewritten:

The contact substance absorbs the reacting gases at its surface.

The sentence now has ten words instead of sixteen and a gain in force and clearness.

Along these lines or *along this line* is condemned by rhetoricians as trite; in technical writing it is useless. It is not precise and usurps the place of a more meaningful phrase.

These analyses were conducted along the same line.
Better: These analyses were made in the same way.

Other phrases outworn, outmoded, and now used to give an impression without committing the author are:

widespread use	in order to
compares favorably	that is to say
holds promise	as stated previously
by means of	it should be understood
for the purpose of	as a matter of fact
revolutionary development	relatively new to the field
significantly reduced	due to the fact that

think in terms of

Such words are indispensable to the writer who does not want to be pinned down or who does not have the information necessary to convince.

The *utilization* of water-cooled air conditioners *for the purpose of* maintaining *an adequate* room temperature and humidity *is practiced by virtually all* plant offices.
Better: Most plant offices use water-cooled air conditioners.

People who say or write "great," "nice," and "fabulous" do so because they have nothing in their minds but the vague pleasurableness suggested by such trite words. To describe character, for example, with words like "unselfish," "finicky," or "calculating" requires the ability to see these qualities with the eye and the mind. To see the weather as "murky" demands a different quality of eyesight from the kind that sees "lousy."

Critics of technical writing have published their annoyance with this style of synthetic, meaningless, confusing writing. Technical report writers can avoid trite words and phrases by saying what they have to say frankly and honestly.

What sort of expression should a writer who wants to avoid the charge of *trite* look for? Most trite expressions will be found to be outworn figures of speech, frayed quotations, attempts at a gentility that the idea does not deserve, or phrases that somehow are found intact more often than is pleasing, especially journalistic combinations of adjectives and nouns.

Euphemism. A *euphemism* is a pale or comfortable word or phrase used instead of the more common or abrupt name for some discomfort or suffering, or for something presumed to be offensive to delicate ears. The substituted expression may be more vague, less harsh in sound or connotation, than the more exact and literal term it displaces; it is often abstract, semilearned, or a Latin derivative instead of the English word.

The largest group of euphemisms has rather a moral than an emotional backing. It consists of substitutes for many short abrupt words, the vigorous monosyllabic names of certain physical functions and social unpleasantness. *Spit* becomes *expectorate; drunk* is *intoxicated;* and even *drink* tends to become *imbibe.* Teeth are *extracted* instead of *pulled. Story* takes the place of *lie,* or in various dialects it is *whopper, fib, misrepresentation.* Both *stink* and *smell* give way to *odor; belly* to *abdomen* and so on. A group of euphemisms has been developed (often purposefully) in the business world:

> *carriage* for *shipping expense*
> *reconditioned* for *second-hand*
> *public relations counsel* for *press agent*
> *repossessed* for *equipment not paid for*
> *image* for *reputation*
> *manufacturer's representative* for *salesman*

Except for these journalistic and commercial terms, and some taboos of the radio and TV networks, the movies, and newspapers, the temper of the times is now against euphemisms in writing, especially technical writing; and unless circumstances actually demand a substitute for the ordinary names of things and situations, a writer should call a spade a spade—simply, of course, without unnecessary emphasis.

Big Words. The term "big words" is used to cover several common faults of writing that come from an unhappy use of words. The words may not all be long or uncommon, but they are big in that they are *too heavy for their place.*

There is little objection to long words when they are called for by the subject and are appropriate to the reader and come naturally to the writer, that is, when they are the words in which he thinks. They are the only and necessary names for many ideas and for many things, and they must be used in technical, scientific, and professional writing—though they may be overused even in the writing of specialists.

Some writers of technical reports never "go" anywhere—they invariably "proceed."

The mixing proceeded smoothly.

Neither do they "begin" work; they "inaugurate" or "initiate" it. Nor do they "get" or "obtain" information; they "secure" it. If the amount of data with which they are working is not large they would not call it "small," but "limited" or "restricted." Their work is not "done," but it is "conducted." That is stuffy writing.

Cacophony. Reading copy aloud is the best way to detect this use of unfortunate words, annoying sounds and rhymes. These phrases divert the reader's attention, break his train of thought, and grate on his sensibilities.

periodical general physical	soft-solder seal
simple sample systems	textual tests
similar system of symbols	candid standards
elemental metals mentioned	prepared preformed performic acid
cessation of saturation	solution for elution
conducted protracted	

To date, data show has a harsh, unpleasant sound. *So far data show* is preferable; simply *data show* is still better. Similarly, *during drying* should be replaced by *while drying*.

Syntax

The meaning of a single word will frequently be influenced heavily by its relationship to other words in the sentence, or its *syntax.*

The busy reader will be easily confused by an uncertain relationship between a word and its antecedent. A few examples of ambiguous constructions of this kind will illustrate how the report writer can misrepresent fact unintentionally.

The next sintered mixture for the experimental heating unit consisted of 77% talc and 23% zinc, but this was unsatisfactory.

The antecedent of "this" is uncertain. Is it the method of mixing and sintering that was unsatisfactory, or the proportion of zinc, or perhaps the use of zinc itself?

Suppose the sentence were modified as follows:

> The next sintered mixture for the experimental heating unit consisted of 77% talc and 23% zinc, but this element was unsatisfactory.

At first glance the meaning of this sentence may appear to be unmistakable—until the possible referents of the word "element" are considered. Which was unsatisfactory, the experimental heating element or the use of the chemical element Zn? A better construction would be:

> The next sintered mixture, consisting of 77% talc and 23% zinc, could not be used as a heating element because volume resistivity was too high with this proportion of talc-zinc.

Of course, the antecedent of "this" in the first example about the sintered mixture might have been clarified by the context. Although the next sentence, paragraph, or section of the report might have explained what was "unsatisfactory," this type of ambiguous sentence structure tends to confuse the reader and to retard the reading process.

Another type of vague wording might not slow the reader at all because he may not even be aware of his misinterpretation.

> All the equipment for this experimental work has not been received. The last delivery date was July 17.

The reader might quickly assume from this that the last time some of the equipment was delivered was July 17, whereas the writer meant the most recent promise for delivery of the remaining equipment was July 17.

Suppose the following construction were used in an attempt to clarify the delivery-date situation:

> All the equipment for this experimental work has not been delivered. The supplier promised to deliver the remaining apparatus on July 17.

This might seem to be an improvement—until the significance of July 17 is considered. Is it the date of promised delivery or the date of the promise itself? A better way of expressing the intended meaning is:

July 17 is the most recent delivery date promised for the remainder of the apparatus.

The above examples were taken from a paper written by an expert in semantics and syntax. Michaelson, H. B., "Semantics and Syntax in Technical Reports," *Chem. Eng. News*, **28**, 2416(1950). The following examples in *Implied Meanings* were taken from the same source.

Implied Meanings. Implied meanings may also cause confusion. In the introductory section of a report, for example, this type of construction is found frequently:

For many years no satisfactory method was known for sealing together these two materials for use in a vacuum system, but seals have now been made successfully.

Where were the good seals first made—as part of this particular development work or in an unrelated recent project?

A more common type of ambiguity is a lack of proper subordination of ideas in a sentence. The skillful writer will ensure clarity of expression by subordinating the dependent clauses and phrases to the main thought. Since this is not done in the following sentence, the meaning is not entirely clear:

The carbon brushes in the motor were badly worn and the centrifuge was inoperative.

By subordinating the less important ideas in the sentence, the relationship between brushes and centrifuge operation is clarified:

Since the carbon brushes in the motor were badly worn, the centrifuge was inoperative.

The misplaced modifier, too, does its share of deceiving the unsuspecting reader. For instance, the placement of the word "only" makes a difference in the meaning of the following two sentences:

He only emptied two flasks.
He emptied only two flasks.

The foregoing examples of faulty syntax show how much clarity of meaning depends on a logical style of writing; careful diction and precise terminology are in vain unless words are put together to express ideas accurately.

Meaning from Context. Besides connotations that are more or less permanent characteristics of words, there are more immediate connotations that come from context, from the way they are used at a specific time or from the other words around them. In speaking, the usual meaning of a word can be altered or even changed by the tone of voice or facial expression or gesture. In writing, the tone is set by the general style and by the tenor of ideas expressed.

Water, for example, may refer simply to a drink, or it may be used to refer to a variety of mixtures used commonly as solvents described from "hard" to "distilled," or it may imply a medium for sports, transportation, or health.

Besides these widespread connotations and those that are clear in the context, there are often special associations a word may have for a particular person—a suggestion that his past experience or his temperament or his ideals or his imagination has given it for him. Making use of the connotations of words gives writing a quality of style that is called *suggestion.* The reader is carried beyond the literal meaning, senses and feeling of the writer, and comes to believe in him as a real person.

Misused Words and Phrases. Such phrases as *from the standpoint of* and *on the basis of* are overused by some writers, who employ them in connections where their propriety may be questioned, *as from the standpoint of pathology, from the viewpoint of road building,* where *pathology* and *road building* are used for *pathologist* and *road builder. From the point of view of doctoring* means *from the doctor's point of view;* it is the person, not the profession, which can have a point of view.

This is too important a matter to be treated from a careless point of view.
Better: This is too important a matter to be treated carelessly.
Based on measurements made on photographs there were six test runs.
Better: From measurements made on photographs, there were six test runs.

The phrase *is responsible for* is improperly used where no responsibility is involved.

A flood from the lab *was responsible for* (caused) this damage.

Former and *latter* are often misused. They should not be employed in a sentence that is so long and involved that the reader will have to look back to find what the words refer to. A good general rule is to repeat the words for which they stand. Of course *former* and *latter* cannot be used if there are more than two antecedents, as in the sentence:

The mixture consists of hydrochloric acid, silicon, and stannous chloride, the former constituting two-thirds of the weight.

These words are used by some writers in a way that absolutely conceals their meaning or the meaning intended, which must be guessed or inferred from the context.

The concentration of the sulfide ion is so greatly affected by change of acidity that the latter (this change?) is the principal factor determining the precipitation of sulfides.

The habitual use of abstract terms like *cases* and *instances* for concrete, clearly significant terms that can easily be understood constitutes one of the worst vices of technical writing.

In the case of the solutions affecting the ionization, they were evidently rich in sodium chloride.
Better: The solutions affecting the ionization were evidently rich in sodium chloride.
As in the case of oil lands, phosphate lands are withdrawn.
Better: Phosphate lands, like oil lands, are withdrawn.

Character, conditions, purposes, and similar words are by some writers habitually intruded into sentences in which they are superfluous or ridiculous, or both.

The surface is of a very uneven character.
Better: The surface is uneven.
The hard nature of the crystals makes them suitable for this purpose.
Better: The hardness of the crystals makes them suitable.

The phrase *a number of* is overworked by many report writers. Probably it is usually intended to mean an indefinite rather small number, in about the same sense as what is generally understood by *several*. But as 7,000,000 or 70,000,000 is also *a number* it seems preferable to use an appropriate and more specific substitute, such as *several* or *a few*.

Some report writers tend to hedge and do not make specific statements about their work or data.

Naphthalene *may, for the time being, be presumed* to be causing *more or less* toxicity in isolated individuals.

A writer of technical reports certainly ought to have more specific data to report.

Develop and *development* are used by technical writers in too many senses. *Developed* is used to mean *occurred, formed, exploited, worked, mined,* or anything else that may happen to be in the mind of the writer who will not take the trouble to think of the word he really needs.

The second reaction has been *developed* (run).
They were *developed* (formed) in greater thickness.
Plants are *present in less abundance and in more stunted development* (less abundant and smaller?).

Proved, not *proven,* is the preferred form of the past tense and the past participle of the verb *prove.*

As a rule *important* is not the most appropriate word unless it is accompanied by some term denoting why or how the thing described is important, as *commercially important.* It should not be used for *abundant, conspicuous, valuable,* or any other word of clearly defined meaning.

The most *important* (best) route is to the west.
The most *important* (abundant) ingredient in this recipe is flour.

Majority is a good term for use at election time. It is improperly used for *most,* as in:

The large majority of grains range up to a quarter of a millimeter.
Some ore has gone to smelters, but *the majority* is here.

Due to is often used carelessly to mean *caused by* or *because of*. Both *due* and *owing* are adjectives and hence must modify nouns, not verbs.

This school was demolished by the earthquake, because (not *due to* the fact that) it stood on made-ground.

After phrases following *for instance, for example, such as,* and similar expressions, *etc.* is not only superfluous but improper, as in the sentence below:

Nembutal is clinically the safest of the barbiturates and is used preoperatively to allay upset emotions, *such as* fear, nervousness, *etc.*

The use of a verb plus a preposition to express an idea that may be conveyed by some other verb alone may lead to the undesirable doubling of prepositions:

The conditions *met with* (observed, prevailing) in the offices were good.
Gastrectomy has been *carried on* (done) on this patient.
This can be *dispensed with* (spared, or omitted) to advantage.

Superfluous and improper words are italicized below:

There can be no doubt *but* that it is explosive.
The conditions were favorable for tuberculosis *to occur*.
It occurs in *disseminated* grains scattered through the cells.
The rock is dark green *in color*.
The weals do not break out *at the surface*.

The phrase *as already stated* is generally unnecessary and undesirable. Repetition of a statement in another connection may be perfectly justifiable, but the reader need not be notified that it is a repetition—in fact, he may not realize it unless the author tells him.

Wordiness. Many sentences can be greatly shortened without loss in clarity or fluency, such as:

The following report deals with a similar investigation of Conroe crude and is offered as a supplement of the aforementioned report on Oklahoma City crude.
Better: The following report on Conroe crude supplements the report on Oklahoma City crude.

Brevity is often lost because of plain wordiness.

It will be seen from the foregoing figures ....
Better: These figures show ....
It would thus appear that this is best.
Better: Apparently this is best.
At an earlier date the reaction failed.
Better: Previously the reaction failed.
Smith conducted treated experiments on the rats.
Better: Smith treated the rats.

George Orwell wrote, "The great enemy of clear language is insincerity. When there is a gap between one's real and one's declared aims, one turns as it were instinctively to long words and exhausted idioms, like a cuttlefish squirting out ink."

Brevity is also lost by the use of redundant expressions, as indicated by italics in the following:

close proximity	anthracite *coal*
final outcome	ascend *up*
as a *general* rule	attach *together*
important essentials	adequate *enough*
necessary requisite	may *possibly*
seeming paradox	square *in shape*
true facts	fuse *together*
blue *in color*	*the year* 1965

The misuse of words and phrases by the slovenly writer makes their proper use less effective. The more careful writer, even with all his care, may fail to convey his ideas clearly to some of his readers because their minds have been dulled by general word misuse.

CHAPTER 13 *Types of Reports*

Many reports fall into an academic rut because an attempt is made to utilize all the parts available with their headings in one document. It is absurd to insist that every report must have an abstract, conclusion, summary, appendix, and illustrations. Naturally, not all these parts are necessary in every report. Which parts are to be used depends upon the type of report which in turn depends upon the time of year, progress of research, whim of the boss, complaint from a customer, or the need for more money. Whatever the names of the reports, they can be lumped into two classes: those that report status and those that report accomplishment.

Status Reports

Many reports must be written to contain certain specified topics, by a certain date, for a select, definite set of readers. Some research directors have a habit of wanting by tomorrow a summary of what has been done during the last couple of weeks. The more orderly managements will require such reports ahead of time on a schedule. No consideration is given to whether the research man is ready to draw conclusions from his data, or whether trends have been established. It is important in managing a research organization that the sponsors have prompt answers to their questions regardless of the research man's mood. Their questions, usually legitimate, are many times political in nature. Someone within or outside the laboratory organization must be well enough informed that, when questioned by others about the status of a specific experiment, pilot plant results, or how certain expenses are met, he will know the answers.

For instance, the chief executive of a company in conference with a government official over letting a contract will telephone his research director, or some similar subordinate, for the information he needs. To show an efficient research organization, the research director must be prepared with a reasonably recent status report.

Administrative decisions will be guided by the status or progress of the projects under way. Emphasis may need changing. Personnel may need shifting. Other research work may hinge on the progress reported. Many times this class of report is written merely to satisfy some accounting requirement, such as justifying additional appropriations, or to satisfy some patent requirement such as corroborating evidence.

All these reasons for requesting a status report are perfectly sound, but each reason will require different treatment by the author. For a patent disclosure, complete details including size of experimental equipment, concentration of materials, times, temperatures, and pressures may be necessary. However, patent people find little interest in reports that discuss theories, show dollar savings, or are filled with recommendations about future work.

To justify a new appropriation no report writer should go into details about the experimental design or anticipated temperatures and pressures unless the conditions were sufficiently extreme to require special equipment.

Those in control of finances for a research project—such as vice president in charge of research, plant manager, treasurer of the company, or technical directors—demand to know the objectives of the project, and "neck-sticking-out" discussions of "promising results." "Appealing possibilities" are called for in these reports. These reports may predict dollar savings and discuss future work. Even if readers of these reports are able to follow details, they don't want them. Of concern to them are what accomplishments are planned with the appropriation or what has been done so far. These men generally can't base their decisions on minute details. If details are of interest they will be asked for. For the writer to supply them each time a report is requested because *this time* the reader might want them only serves to annoy busy executive readers.

These men are usually willing to be sold. They are "research-minded." The extra effort spent by a writer in showing the advantages and the potentials when requesting appropriations will be rewarded many more times than if the writer spent considerable technical man-hours copying experimental details from his notebook. The executive reader is impressed not by the quantity of words but by the selling quality of the report. Here is the place for the technical writer to be imaginative and creative; he may even use figures of speech to prove a point. Metaphors suggest more than they actually state. This method of writing by comparison often orients non-technical readers without insulting their intelligence by "writing down" to them.

The technical writer who writes a good report asking for an appropriation uses a thing called "double vision." Many technical men look at one thing, and see it as just that one thing: they do not instinctively notice resemblances. But a gifted scientist will watch crystals coalesce, a snowstorm, or a girl's face and be reminded of something else. This type of comparison can appear in appropriation reports.

Stephen Leacock wrote an imaginative description of today's schools. "Modern colleges keep books like ledgers in which the student is reduced to credits, merits, hours per week, and weeks per year. They can fill him out in five minutes as sixty percent Christian, forty-five percent normal, assiduity guaranteed up to fourteen hours a day—saturation point—and intelligence tested five times under pressure and never burst."

Metaphors and similes must be visually sharp, and mysteriously imaginative. They will almost always be something of a surprise. One of the best tests to apply is the statement, "Why, I never thought of that before." If you can say this, and at the same time be impressed with the appropriateness of the similarity, then the metaphor is good.

Reports of status have been called by many names such as: Interim Report, Progress Report (Daily, Weekly, Monthly, Quarterly, Semiannual, and Annual), Special Report, Status Report, Research Proposal, as well as some truly unprintable names.

Reports of status are the kind of reports that are usually anathema to research report writers. Frequently they are requested at a most inconvenient time; they usually are written against a deadline. As the readers almost always have varied backgrounds, much effort is required of the writer to avoid terms too technical, mathematics too imposing, and objectives that might seem too imaginative to a stockholder, a congressman, an accountant, or a production manager.

A status report's most valuable characteristic is its *timeliness*. Adherence to firm deadlines is extremely important. Requesting money after the budget is approved is not too successful. Long delays in editing, typing, reproduction, and distribution often destroy the usefulness of these reports. Report writing has gathered considerable disfavor, largely caused by the issuing of obsolescent status reports. The reason for writing the report may have disappeared with the passage of time. For instance, the Annual Report of the department may have gone to press; costs may have gone up; customers may have been lost.

These reports should be written as well as possible, not dashed off and forgotten; but they must not be late. Since timeliness is such an important factor, the author may be permitted some laxness in formality in favor of accomplishing the purpose of rapid communication.

One form of laxity in formality that may be permitted in reporting status as quickly as possible is the use of first person singular and plural:

> We cannot conclude from these meager data, but I believe we can draw conclusions next month.

Another divergence from strict formality may be applied to the illustrations. Curves and sketches prepared by the author on translucent paper with reasonable care will permit cheap diazo reproductions (Ozalid). The convenience of this simple system of duplicating line drawings and curves is an asset which can permit the liabilities of high costs per individual page, frequent background tone, and slightly increased paper thickness.

There are other informalities that can be allowed, and authors and their managements should judge for themselves the price in time that they wish to pay for tardiness, involved in preparing a finished, formal status report.

Research or Technical Proposals. A special case of the status report is the *proposal*. Timeliness is the criterion. A late proposal is seldom even considered. Proposals are special because they are really sales documents although, in most cases, highly technical.

Each proposal you prepare must be tailor-made for its audience. What is right for one proposal may well be completely wrong for another. Individuality is the price that will win contracts.

In July, 1961, Emil Skocpol discussed technical proposal writing before the Fourth Annual Institute in Technical and Industrial Communications at Colorado State University. Some of this material on writing proposals was taken from Skocpol's talk.

Any written piece of communication that attempts to sell an idea, concept, piece of equipment, or anything else is a proposal. What the boss likes and dislikes; what his favorite color is; whether price, or quality or meeting deadlines impresses him most are critical for most report writing. The same things need to be known about the customers who are to receive the proposal. They want to hear a certain tune played and the tune should be played just as sweetly and as harmoniously as possible. People who evaluate very many proposals know most of the tricks and evasions. So the proposal writer is forced to be forthright when writing a proposal or any technical report. Today most companies do not wish to disclose *everything* in a proposal because the very nature of a proposal makes it a confidential and proprietary communication from one party to another, and violations of this confidence and idea-pirating have caused much aggravation and dissatisfaction.

Cordial relations depend on many things, but the confidence of the party submitting the proposal can be retained only if his interests are protected. The competitive factor makes it mandatory that, for the protection of the proposer, his information and his particular approach to the solution of the problem be respected and not be made available to possible competitors, except through financial arrangements.

Some proposers have been disenchanted by certain experiences and have felt that small companies with good minds have been brain-picked, that their proposals have been used in parts and put together into a query that has gone out to larger companies, and that ultimately the larger, rather than the smaller companies whose composite proposal ideas were used, obtained contracts. Between an agency that has problems and solicits solutions to those problems by means of proposals and those who submit through proposals, confidence must be established on sound footing. It will require a reorientation or a reaffirmation of agency philosophy in some cases. All these considerations merely indicate obstacles that exist in the way of dissemination of material contained in the technical parts of proposals.

Many technical writers today write major proposals to government agencies or prime contractors of government agencies. These proposals are on systems, subsystems, or equipment. The technical proposal in some cases is composed of many, sometimes many dozens of documents, protracted over a long period of time. But for the purpose of simplicity a proposal is referred to here as one document. This document, usually accompanied by a cost bid, is an offer by a business firm or scientist to solve engineering or scientific problems for a customer.

The proposal has a dual purpose: (1) It must convey information, and (2) It must instill a favorable attitude toward that information.

The requirements for style, organization, and technique are high, but the penalties for failure are higher.

The use of proposals as a selling tool is becoming more important, and proposals will become more complex as future sales systems become more sophisticated.

J. Frank Epstein, of Hughes Aircraft Company, recently surveyed fifteen major companies in the aerospace industry. These companies had prepared more than 5,000 new-business proposals in the past year. Fourteen of the fifteen companies said the number of research proposals being selected for bid is increasing. Epstein further learned that "companies in the aerospace industry assign their most capable personnel to direct proposal preparation."

The key contribution to a technical proposal is sound and imaginative engineering design or program plan. The facts never speak for themselves. They must be carefully selected, arranged, welded together, and presented in language and sequence that the reader will not only understand effortlessly, but also enjoy and admire. Effective organization and styling in a proposal may do much to increase its chances of success. It is even possible that a less-than-first-rate-technical solution can be "sold" to a customer through effective presentation.

Unfortunately, being effective includes more than just presenting sound facts with clarity. The questions in the customer's mind must be answered, and answered in such a way to create a favorable opinion. Know the customer; have empathy for him. (See Chapter 2)

The cover makes the first impression on the reader and should arouse his interest in reading the proposal. Obviously it is impractical to design a separate cover for each proposal. A basic cover that fulfills general needs can be used in most cases. As a minimum, the cover should have space for the proposal number, title, date, and address of the recipient. It should provide a white space area for security classification and proprietary data notices. References to the proposal request and other activities preceding the submission of the proposal may be included. In special cases a cover designed to sell your company's qualifications on the particular program most effectively should be created. Otherwise, some other dramatic design should be used. Color is almost a necessity. It will add less than five percent to the cost and may add twenty to fifty percent to the impact.

If a standard cover is used, the impact of your proposal may be increased by using a dramatic illustration of a customer benefit as a frontispiece.

The specific format for each proposal should be selected to fit its requirements. In proposals of over two hundred pages, all the major sections will be required. Some of the sections may be large enough to demand binding in separate volumes. The proposal sections are: (1) cover, (2) front matter (table of contents), (3) summary, (4) introduction, (5) statement of task, or statement of the problem, (6) technical description, proposed approach, technical approach, or technical analysis, (7) management plan, or program organization, (8) program plan or schedule, (9) conclusions, (10) capabilities and experience, or qualifications, (11) personnel résumés, (12) facilities and equipment, and (13) appendixes. Other sections may be specification compliance, reliability organization and program, and test program and plan. In proposals of less than fifty pages, many of the sections would be eliminated, and others combined.

According to people who make evaluations, the most frequent fault in unsuccessful proposals is over-simplification of the technical requirement or problems. Consider: Here are people who have gone to a lot of thought and work preparing specifications; they are willing to expend a good deal of money for the services of someone to solve their problem, so if they are told that a supplier can do this just as easily as falling off a log, the supplier may be making light of something that the customer feels quite seriously about. So they do not believe that the problem is fully understood and look elsewhere.

Proposal evaluators are seldom led to the right conclusions by generalities that are not backed up by specific facts.

Some faults common to proposals throughout industry are more closely related to the technical writer's primary tasks of outlining, rewriting, and reorganizing:

(1) Look out for padding, repetition, overlapping, duplication.

(2) Eliminate discrepancies—both in fact and form.

(3) Avoid repeating or using the exact words, information, etc. contained in the "RFP" and the specification.

(4) Use simple present or future sentence construction.

The proposal is a sales document, but avoid the glowing self-praise route of most magazine advertisements. Those that do not, lose the game. The basic objective is to give the customer the answers to his scientific and engineering problems—answers at a minimum of cost and a minimum of risk.

A conclusions and recommendation section is a hangover from

report writing; it can be left out unless there are compelling reasons for including them. Nothing is less effective than a final section that restates a few nothings that probably never should have been said.

List the performing personnel, with their education and experience qualifications; include only those persons now employed who are, or will be, assigned to work on the proposed program. High-powered lists of project engineers and section leaders for a simple job is obviously "boiler plate."

The customer is vitally interested in details of the organization planned for his job. He should be advised whether a special group will be formed or whether company-wide participation is planned. Explain how and by whom the program will be managed. If a special project group is to be assembled, outline the limits of its authority and responsibility. Also show its position in the company organization and its relationship to other segments of the company. If such a project group is not planned, identify the management, engineering, and staff groups to be involved, and briefly describe their proposed method of operations.

Deal in a straightforward and precise manner with such subjects as handling bottle-necks which can be foreseen, overcoming delays which cannot be anticipated, expediting lagging segments of the program, and precautionary and insurance measures taken to avoid overruns and late deliveries.

What of rejected proposals that might contain valuable scientific, engineering, and research information? Siegfried Mandel answers this very nicely in his paper, "The Proposal" (*Proc. 1963 Inst. Tech. Ind. Commun.* p. 59).

The academic researcher and industrial proposer who have confidence in their ideas and have put time and energy into the proposal will not permit it to go to waste.

Write-ups developed for specific proposals are edited and converted into "boiler plate" which is used for standard routine prequalification proposals that are constantly submitted to a large number of government agencies by some companies. When new specific inquiries come into the company office, the boiler plate often forms a satisfactory rough draft for the working proposal. This is a sensible way of retrieving information, avoiding costly duplication of proposal work, and it permits the company to be ready as proposal deadlines approach.

However, the very factors that may enter into the rejection of a proposal by one agency may be no deterrent in others, and ultimately there is someone for whom the proposal may be of significance.

The report by Robert K. Shnitzler, "Making Your Technical Proposals More Effective," (*STWP Review*, 10(2), 2(1963); ibid. 10(3), 7) will be helpful to report writers who must plan and present a technical proposal.

Accomplishment Reports

When a technical man has accomplished something and the desire to tell others is "in his bones," one of the media of expression is the accomplishment report. A partial list of the names by which these reports are known is:

application survey	preliminary evaluation
biographical résumé	procedure manual
call report	recommendation report
design report	sales service report
final report	suggested procedure
instruction manual	survey report
market survey	tentative process report
operating manual	terminal report
operation survey	trip report

These reports are prepared when the writer has something to say —when his research has reached a reportable point. They contain all the available topics, facts, and opinions, and are usually written for a general, indefinite set of readers.

When research work has reached a stage where a coherent story may be told with conclusions, even though tentative, timeliness becomes subordinate to formality. This class of report may be timeless. The great works of scientific literature fall into this category, such as Darwin's "Origin of Species" and Newton's "Principia."

In many laboratories accomplishment reports are used as manuscripts to be submitted to technical journals for publication. In a practical sense, the most important readers of these reports are within the organization, and propriety demands that they read the report before publication.

Often these readers will be the ones who approve the treatise for publication. Careful writing of the report may permit large sections to be used verbatim in journals.

Special care must be taken with illustrations; tables, graphs, charts, drawings, and photographs should be prepared with the thought in mind that they may be lifted bodily for inclusion later in a manuscript to a journal.

Fifty percent of the unclassified accomplishment reports containing publishable data prepared by Government agencies find their way in one form or another into the technical press within six months.

Many accomplishment reports will never be submitted to a technical journal. Some are classified as valuable to the nation's security. Some are classified as valuable to a company's "know-how." Some report essentially negative results; indeed, the establishment of a *Journal of Negative Results* has frequently been advocated.

Unfortunately, there are also those accomplishment reports that are not worthy of having their readership broadened.

Reports of accomplishment are written when the results justify reporting, and, though they may be more satisfying to write, are frequently deemed less important in the day-to-day conduct of a research organization than the reports of status.

After a paper has been completed, it should be reviewed by one or more separate reviewers or by a committee. Many authors seem to consider such a review to be an unwarranted impertinence, and they approach it with various bewildering psychological defenses, ranging from, "Here I am. Crucify me!" to "Do you wanna fight?" Needless to say, such attitudes are absurd. Submitting a manuscript to a reviewer should not be to exhibit the author's own brilliance as against the reviewer's wickedness and stupidity, but only to make the paper more readable and more accurate scientifically.

All comments and suggestions should be carefully considered. Some of them may be incorrect or may indicate that the reviewer has not understood. In such cases, the reviewer should not be scolded, but an attempt should be made to determine where he was misled and to consider whether others might be similarly misled. If an appreciable likelihood exists, the material should be so revised that this danger will be minimized. Remember at all times that a report should be clear and that the reviewer is probably a typical reader—or is at least typical of a considerable proportion of readers. The fact that a passage can be explained to his satisfaction does not mean that the passage is satisfactory; it must be written so that it will be clear to the reader even when the author is not present to explain it.

Sometimes the reviewer will make an important technical contribution to a report, such as a clearly superior method of developing an equation. Such contributions should be accepted. Responsibility of the author to the reader is still paramount. It may be appropriate, however, to acknowledge the reviewer's contribution in the text, to ask him to write an appendix under his own name, or even to make him a coauthor.*

An accomplishment report is a complete *treatise* on a given subject.

The treatise has a broader class of readership. There should be sections included for all types of readers. The abstract is for the hurried reader and the literature searchers who want a capsule report. Words are precious here. Be brief. Avoid repeating. If redundancy is necessary for clarity, it should come later, in the body of the report.

Conclusions and recommendations will be read by many more people than the details. Readers of scientific and technical matter use these sections as newspaper readers use headlines—to decide whether or not to read the body of the report. More work should be devoted to the proper wording of these sections than of any other part of the report.

When the report is written and ready for typing, every report writer must reread his introduction and edit it. He will lengthen it or shorten it; he may rewrite it since the report he has just written has given him a clearer insight than he ever had before into the accomplishment he has just reported.

---

* From S. Katzoff, "Clarity in Technical Reporting," 2nd ed., Scientific and Technical Information Division, National Aeronautics and Space Administration, Washington, D.C., 1964.

The treatise report is a valuable tool of all research workers. When the report is finished, it may be useful to many readers. It may stimulate creative thought; it may lead to the production of some new material or equipment; it may save a corporation or government bureau the construction or purchase of some useless, but costly, factory or product. Above all, it has clarified the author's thinking about his completed project.

Biographical Résumé. A type of report not often considered as technical writing, is the biographical résumé. Many of the concepts involved in technical report writing should be inculcated in résumé preparation. The use of a résumé as introductory to an interview for employment is also not the only use for résumés.

Although the use of the résumé for seeking employment is by far the most important to the individual, a new use is becoming increasingly important to the employer. This new use is the description of the people who will be assigned to perform work described in the Technical Contract Proposals. Here is a case of an accomplishment report being a section of a status report. Billions of dollars are awarded annually by industry and the Government on the basis of the excellence of written proposals. The Department of Defense has emphasized the importance they place on the biographies in these proposals.

A biographical résumé is in a sense an advertisement. Its purpose when used for employment is to obtain an interview. When it is used in a proposal it is a device to show technical competence. To be sure, technical competence must be obvious when submitting the résumé for a job. It is not more important, however, than obtaining the interview. If the résumé is sufficiently attractive to a prospective employer to initiate an invitation for interview, the opportunity for displaying further technical competence is available when the parties are face to face.

Personnel people insist that the following other considerations should be met when submitting a résumé to a prospective employer:

(1) The résumé should always be accompanied by a cover-letter.

(2) It should always appear to be an original—no carbon copies.

(3) Qualifications should be weighted to meet the job description. Sweeping claims must be carefully supported.

(4) Don't oversell. Long paragraphs describing experience obtained during a brief, prior employment engender antagonism.

(5) Be very brief. Use a tabular form, not narrative, and thus show consideration for the reader's time.

(6) Avoid gaps in the employment record.

(7) Point out limitations in as positive a manner as possible—but be honest. (If you have a speech difficulty, say so.)

(8) Avoid spelling errors at all costs. Poor spelling is the number one complaint about résumés from personnel people.

(9) Flood the market at once. Do not try a few prospective employers at a time. It limits your choice.

These bits of advice are consistent with the general report writing rules of:

(1) Have empathy for your reader.

(2) Have an introduction—set the stage.

(3) Be concise.

(4) Use illustrations or tables to express your data.

An excellent reference is by E. C. Gruber, "Résumés That Get Jobs" (Arco Pub. Co., New York, 1963).

The appearance, the grammar, the sequence (from the last job to the first) the accuracy, the detail (exact salary and dates) all reflect the personality of the individual. And there are few people who can prepare excellent résumés of themselves casually. They require thought, planning, time for gathering the data, a cooling off period, editing, and persuasiveness. The obvious interest in appealing to the reader should be carried over into all report writing.

There are a number of companies who specialize in performing a service for those seeking employment. They are specialists in résumé writing. Employers have strong feelings about these experts. If the résumé is very obviously professionally done, even to the point of including a by-line, it may very well appeal to the ego of the applicant, but generally the employer is antagonized by this professionalism. On the other hand, there are professional résumé writers who do everything possible to see that the applicant gets an invitation for interview, by putting his professional experience to work for the applicant.

Employers who receive a well prepared résumé and a literate cover letter have grown to expect that the author will be a good report writer on the job. A good report writer thinks clearly.

Professor C. W. Foulk, grand old man of the Department of Chemistry at The Ohio State University, has said, "The English language is the most important scientific instrument at your disposal. Learn to use it with precision."

Report writers often bemoan the necessity of writing. Most of the moaners do not realize the amount of research thinking they engage in during the preparation of a treatise-type report. They object to the readership, to the necessity for good grammar, to the problem of organizing their report and checking it when finished. These problems are the price scientists pay for the opportunity of sitting down at a desk with their notes and thinking about their accomplishments in a precise, orderly way.

Report writers should know that no book or report can sustain interest where the reader's knowledge equals the writer's and there is no new light to be shed.

Technical reporting is one of the most exacting mental disciplinary measures of science. The freedom to publish research carries the responsibilties of accuracy in fact and expression. Remove publication rights from scientists and the entire fraternity suffers. Care in the use of writing as a research tool is as essential to the scientists as care in the use of any other delicate laboratory tool.

The objective of this book is not an end in itself; the goal is an expansive one. The goal is a way of seeing that will spread through a technical writer's life, from thinking to writing, to empathy for readers, to studying, to emotion, and to inspiration in reports. As one technical man described it, "In the process of learning to write, I developed an entirely new way of looking at human experience and laboratory experiments, which are really closely related."

Thinking people do not look at life in a sloppy, hurried way. It is the intense, concentrated way that distinguishes artists, philosophers, scientists, and superior men of business—the way of all tense, sensitive, and thoughtful men and women.

When you have learned to translate accurate, visual images into precise, suggestive language you are truly a technical writer.

TYPES OF REPORTS

CHAPTER 14   *A Model Report*

Mr. C. C. Hargis, Jr. of Goodyear Aerospace Corporation, Akron, Ohio, published the following report in *STWP Review,* 10(3), 2(1963). This paper not only describes a new medium for the technical writer, but is a well-written example of a typical technical report.

This report meets most of the requirements of good report writing. The divisions are well chosen and well ordered. It has an abstract, an illustration, and a bibliography, as well as an introduction, a body with good subheads, and a conclusion. Most important is the fact that the author has succeeded in presenting his message to his readers both clearly and concisely—a task seldom accomplished with such balance.

Finally, the subject of this paper is one with which all technical writers should be familiar. They may never write a scenario for a film; but the possibility of writing a commentary for a technical film should remain in the minds of all those faced with the task of technical report writing.

The Technical Film—An Opportunity for the Technical Writer *
C. C. HARGIS, JR.

Today's mushrooming technology has placed new demands on the technical presentations group for a wide range of media to transmit the desired information most effectively. One medium that has recently come into its own is the technical film, which offers the technical writer a challenging change from the routine of handbooks, reports, and proposals. And yet the same

* Reprinted from October 1963 issue of *STWP Review,* Journal of the Society of Technical Writers and Publishers.

basic skills he already possesses can be used in writing and directing the
technical film. A summary of the principal techniques he will need to know
is given in this article

Writing and directing a motion picture offers the technical writer
a stimulating change of pace and an opportunity to grow professionally. The opportunity exists in the business film, which has ma-
tured from its traditional role in extravagant public relations to a
practical, effective tool in technical communications. Today, films
are being used as visual aids for proposals, progress reports, test
programs, training, and engineering sales. The result in many companies is an increasing demand for the technical-film writer-director who can coordinate the efforts of the activity authorizing the
film and of the in-house or outside film production group.

This article describes briefly some of the elementary principles
and techniques of technical-film script writing. The bibliography
at the end includes sources of information on related aspects, such
as direction, production, and film mechanics.

Planning the Script

Before writing a script, you should first determine the audience
and purpose of the film and do research on the subject matter. The
activity authorizing the film should have the answers to your questions or know where to find them. The questions must be specific
to avoid additional costs later by the discovery that writer and
management failed to communicate during the planning stage.

For instance, is the purpose of the film to sell the subject product,
or is the product to be presented as an example of the company's
capabilities in a particular field? (In the words of the dramatist:
what is the theme of your film?) Will the film be shown chiefly to
one type of audience, such as specialists in the subject matter, or
will it be shown to many types? And how long will the film run?
With concrete answers to these questions, you are ready to begin
your research of the subject matter.

As in most writing assignments, you will want to read a number
of reports, sales brochures, etc., on the subject and interview many
specialists, usually within your own company. You also should

visit the areas where the filming ("shooting") will take place. Here you can learn still more about the subject from the people who will be the "actors" in the film. Be sure to have a cameraman go along to advise you on the mechanical aspects of script planning, such as camera lens angles, size of the area to be filmed, and floor space for setting up camera equipment.

All this time you should be making careful notes and gradually fitting them into an outline compatible with the objectives of the film. The notes can include sketches that you think might be helpful references when you actually begin writing the script. An example is a floor plan showing locations of equipment or the sequence of an operation.

Writing the Script

The typical film script is arranged in two columns (Figure 1). The scene description is at the left, the narration at the right. As to which comes first in the actual writing depends on the writer's personal working habits or the circumstances of the film, or both. Some writers begin with a story treatment, which is simply a narrative-type outline describing in general what will appear on the screen and what the narrator will talk about.

One author in the field writes the story (narrative) first, then thinks of scenes to go with the story (see item by Murray in Bibliography). Such an approach may not be feasible for the entire film, especially when your customer (the authorizing activity) has firm ideas about what to emphasize, such as unique features of a new product.

Sometimes the reverse is true: if certain information must be included in the narration (e.g., the company's 10 years' experience in a certain product line), you must create a picture to fill the screen during that part of the narration. To avoid one long scene or a monotonous pan shot (horizontal sweeping with the camera) just to cover a long paragraph, you can call for shots of art work (sketches, charts, etc.), conferences, still photographs, turning book pages, entrance signs, or other scenes you can draw from your own imagination. One of the motions in motion pictures is the persistent changing of the picture. The change can be a new scene, a different view of the same scene, or a switching back and forth ("cutting") between two scenes.

One principle of film writing is that the narration is subordinate to the scenes. About 75 percent of a film's effectiveness is in the pictures. So the film writer's guiding principle is: *fit the words to the picture*. Use words to separate, explain, or clarify the picture. Write for the ear, not the eye. That is, write short sentences with a conversational flavor and repeat key words as often as necessary for clarity.

Some departure from conventional sentence structure may be necessary. In film writing, the inverted subject-predicate construction and the sentence fragment are commonplace. For evidence, watch documentary films or commercials on television and concentrate on the narration. Then notice how the picture becomes so absorbing that the exact grammatical structure of the narration is no longer apparent.

Another principle of film writing is the predominant use of the present tense (see Figure 1). To the motion-picture audience, the events on the screen are taking place now. An occasional reminder that they actually occurred in the past is all right, but, in general, a film is more effective when events of the past are described in relation to the motion picture of the present. Someone has summed up the principle of present tense thus: never tell what's going to happen ("You are about to see . . ."), seldom tell what has happened, and usually tell what is happening.

A third principle of film writing is that no film—not even a technical one—should be too technical or too detailed. A film is a visual aid, not a substitute, for an oral or printed presentation. The viewer cannot hold a film in his hands and examine it the way he can a book or report. Both words and pictures of a film are fleeting. They change every few seconds, moving on and on. Also, technical films inevitably are shown to not-so-technical audiences, despite the customer's insistence that showings will be limited. For this reason, you should confine the narration to main points only. If you use a new or unusual term, make sure it is explained by the narrator, the picture, or both. A long-winded narration accompanied by static, uninteresting scenes can prevent a film from being the exciting, effective communication medium it is capable of being.

Scene	Narration
33. Close-up, reflector	Thirty feet in diameter, the precision-made reflector is within a few thousandths of an inch of a true parabolic curve.
34. Close-up, antenna motors	Servo motors work in opposition for very accurate tracking at slow rates.
35. Long shot, antenna rotating in azimuth . . .	For faster scanning, the motors work together. In the search mode, the antenna operates three hundred sixty degrees in azimuth . . .
. . . then in elevation	. . . and in elevation from zero to one hundred eighty degrees.
36. Extreme close-up of panel, hand selects bar and spiral modes	After the operator selects a scanning pattern, the antenna functions in that pattern automatically.
37. Antenna rotating, reverses direction	Control is so precise that back-lash and overshooting have been virtually eliminated.
38. Antenna and approaching airplane	The search mode is demonstrated in an operational test. A beacon signal is transmitted from an airplane . . .
39. Long shot, airplane	
40. Antenna tracking	

FIGURE 1. Typical film script.

Getting Approvals

Before authorizing any filming, submit your completed master script to management for review and approval. Often this procedure consists of forwarding it to the customer, who then is responsible for getting all the necessary approvals. In subsequent script conferences, which you should attend, differences of opinion as to treatment, content, etc., can be resolved, including those scenes and narration considered mandatory.

Approval of the master script means only that filming can begin. Final approval will take place at a sneak preview of the completed rough-cut film with a live or tape-recorded narration.

Preparing the Shooting Script

From the approved master script, you will want to prepare a shooting script to use as a checklist on location. In the master script, the scenes are arranged to tell a story, but in the shooting script the same scenes are listed in groups according to each shooting location. (Those sketches made during the planning stage will be especially helpful at this time.) The shooting script also notes the camera field (long shot, medium shot, close-up, etc.) and the length of each scene in seconds.

Grouping the scenes by location keeps to a minimum the number of moves made by the camera crew and their bulky equipment. (In Figure 1, scenes 33 to 35 were filmed in a test building, scene 36 at a control panel located in a second building, and scenes 38 to 40 at an outdoor test site.) With such grouping you are also less likely to miss any scenes, some of which may appear in several places in the film.

To determine the time required for each scene, read the narration aloud, at a moderate pace, and time each segment with a stop watch. The result is the minimum number of seconds needed to cover the narration only. You must arrange for the cameraman to shoot each scene several seconds beyond the calculated time to allow for the starting and stopping of the camera, for optical effects (dissolves, fadeouts, etc.) in the finished film, and for the narrator's normal pauses between sentences and scenes.

Although you will work directly from the shooting script, take a copy of the master script with you. If a certain scene turns out to be unavailable for shooting, you can check the narration on the master script before deciding upon a substitute.

Revising the Script

You will have to revise your master script at least three times: during the filming, during the film editing, and during the recording of the narration. The principle each time is the same: be flexible; make changes as they occur to you. Remember that the script written and approved before the filming is just the first draft. It is a firm, but not rigid, guide to making the film.

When filming finally begins, changes in the script are inevitable. If a shop operation planned to last 5 seconds takes twice as long, film the entire sequence and make a note to add more narration if necessary. If you see something that would add interest or improve upon a scene called for in the script, instruct the camera crew to get a shot of it. If a scene suddenly becomes superfluous because of new information gained on location, delete it from the script.

More revisions will be necessary after the film editor has rough-cut and spliced the processed film according to the master script. During the subsequent cutting and trimming, some scenes will have to be made shorter than the minimum required by the narration, perhaps because one actor fumbles during a production operation, or another looks straight at the camera. Other scenes will be left intact because of their general excellence or rearranged for smoother continuity. By working closely with the film editor, you can note all these changes on the master script as they take place.

Scenes and narration will have to be checked again and again. Once more you concentrate on fitting the words to the picture, which you now have before you on a projector or editing device. You make sure that the opening words of each new scene introduce, identify, or locate the scene. You time the script again, or read it aloud while the film is being projected. You check for crowded or hurried narration. Too much talking can ruin any motion picture, so you cut and polish the words to give the narrator time to pause and the audience time to enjoy the picture and absorb the words. A typical rule of thumb is that the total narration should equal about two-thirds of the film's total running time.

The words also should fit the pace and mood of the pictures. Fast-paced events need appropriately short, snappy phrases and sentences. One technique consists of cueing parts of one sentence to several short scenes—perhaps even one word for each scene. The words should be subordinate to the picture, not compete with it. For example, the narrator should not describe the obvious. When a technician in the close-up scene tightens a panel with a screwdriver, the narrator could say, "No special tools are needed to assemble and disassemble the control panel," rather than "The control panel is fastened with a screwdriver."

The ultimate test of a film script takes place when a competent narrator reads it aloud into a microphone. This is the third period of a script revision. A good narrator can quickly detect too many sibilants bunched together, too many "-tion" endings, or unintended rhymes. Listen carefully to his suggestions. Remember that you wrote the script for an audience that will be depending on his oral delivery.

Conclusion

The opportunity to write and direct a technical film is one that the ambitious technical writer seeking variety in his work cannot afford to pass by. The major qualifications are the skill and self-confidence that should come through experience on other technical-writing assignments. When Catherine Drinker Bowen, the Pulitzer-prize-winning biographer, agreed with some reluctance to cover the Kentucky Derby for a newspaper, she was relieved to find that she could do the job after all, simply by applying her basic knowledge of the craft of writing.

Bibliography

Baddeley, Hugh, "How to Edit Amateur Films," Focal Press, London and New York, 1958. (Good background reading for professional film writer.)

Buchanan, Andrew, "Film-making from Script to Screen," Phoenix House, Ltd., London. (See especially the chapters on writing, the director, documentaries, and filming a factory.)

Kirsch, Maurice, "How to Write Commentaries for Films," Focal Press, London and New York, 1956. (Clear, interesting discussion of principles of script writing.)

Livingston, Don, "Film and the Director," the Macmillan Company, New York, 1953. (*Must* reading for technical-film writer-director; excellent information on scene movements and cuts.)

Murray, Ronald M., "Technical Films—A Luxury or a Necessity," *IRE Transactions on Engineering Writing and Speech*, EWS-1, pp. 31-36, March 1958. (Discusses film costs, writing style, and fitting pictures to the words.)

Smith, Richard W., "Technical Writing," College Outline Series No. 43,
Barnes and Noble, Inc., New York, 1963. (Chapter on film writing stresses
importance of visual imagination and scene pacing.)

Spottiswoode, Raymond, "Film and Its Techniques," University of California
Press, Berkeley and Los Angeles, 1957. (Highly technical background reading on cameras, film, color, sound, etc.; useful bibliography and glossary.)

CHAPTER 15 *Reporting Out Loud*

Science and technology advance by the communication of ideas.
When a scientist or engineer has completed some phase of his work
he may be asked to write a progress report or a paper for publication, and to give the report orally to a group of fellow scientists or
engineers. When an author presents his paper orally he follows the
pattern of any written technical report. Of course, when his talk is
to a club, school salesmen, or customers there will be more emphasis
on explaining the significance of scientific facts, or telling about
what kind of work he and his fellow scientists and engineers do in
industry. Or the emphasis may be on a process or machine, on fire
and health hazards in specific situations, or on use of a certain
product. Emphasis and viewpoint must be decided upon and kept
in mind while organizing the information to be presented in an
oral report. The report writer—in this case, the speaker—must
know why he is going to talk.

The speaker presents a professional paper because he has done
something new or interesting, or because he knows more about a
subject than do his fellow engineers or scientists. He wants to convey useful information for the benefit of his profession and to
increase his own professional standing and prestige. Such an exchange of information is basic to all engineering and scientific progress. No matter how valuable the work done, the speaker's whole
presentation falls flat unless he succeeds in transferring his ideas
and knowledge to the people in the audience.

The speaker is giving his talk to convey useful information. If
he fails, not only has he wasted his time—more important, he has

wasted the time of everyone who came to hear him. The speaker has a very real obligation to his listeners. They expect to be instructed, and they have a legitimate complaint if the speaker fails them. Too many scientists and engineers act as if the audience had no choice but to listen. So it is important for the speaker to know why he is talking—to convey useful information.

Most speakers need (1) better organization and writing for oral delivery and (2) greater care in preparing visual aids, mainly slides. A successful oral presentation before any technical group contains three fundamental elements. (1) It is based upon a technically sound paper oriented and organized for a particular audience. (2) It is delivered concisely and clearly; without details, but with emphasis on significance. (3) If it is illustrated, effective slides or other visuals must aid understanding. More attention by speakers to these fundamental elements will lift many presentations from the mediocre to the excellent class.

Organization

To be worthwhile, a speaker's talk must contribute to the knowledge of the listeners. It also must have enough value to justify the time and expense involved for those who come to hear it. Moreover, as a tool for communicating ideas, the talk must be clearly organized. It may be organized to tell the audience these four things:

(1) Introduction—Why was action taken?
(2) Investigation—What did the speaker do?
(3) Interpretation—What did the speaker learn?
(4) Conclusion—What does it all mean?

These questions are answered in better oral or written scientific reports. Most oral reports make a sharper and more lasting impact when the emphasis is on the first and last of these four points.

A speaker should not try to impress his audience with the depth of his knowledge or the extent of his vocabulary. He ought to seek instead to convey as much useful information as possible. He makes a far better impression when he does so than when he tries to startle people by the intricacy of his subject. Speakers who give useful information are sought out again and again by other engineers and scientists. So the speaker's first task is not to gather together all of his data so that not a single detail is missing, but rather to think over his subject and to decide just what progress he has made or what new ideas he has developed.

Details such as numerical data have their place, of course, in the technical talk; but the speaker must make clear whether the numbers are of such fundamental importance that they should be remembered as such, whether they are presented for comparison with other numbers, as in showing trends or agreement between theory and experiment, or whether they are presented merely to show the thoroughness or the scope of the speaker's work (as when the research consists of determining large quantities of design data).

An audience of technical people is usually composed of those with a broad range of interests and capabilities. If the speaker directs his story to the advanced segment of his audience, he will lose the interest of the less knowledgeable. Since most audiences are composed of more people who have come to learn than of specialists, the speaker will convey more information if he keeps his story simple.

Keeping his story simple doesn't mean that he must strip his talk of its true professional worth. Instead, it means that he should present facts in an easy-to-follow sequence. He may begin with what was sought, and the means available to obtain this information. From here he may proceed to tests conducted, findings of each test, results of each test, and then significance of the tests.

A simple story is one that proceeds from the known to the unknown. Speakers should try to follow this line of thought every time they present a professional paper in a talk.

Edward J. Hegarty has given many speeches and written several excellent books about talking before audiences. His latest, "Red-Hot Public Speaking," * is full of helpful material for giving a polished, professional report out loud. This book is a worthwhile addition to any speechmaker's library. Mr. Hegarty suggests that a speaker choose one of six schemes for organizing his speech. Each scheme fits a specific audience or specific type of oral report.

* From the book "Red-Hot Public Speaking," by Edward J. Hegarty. © 1961 by Prentice-Hall, Inc., Englewood Cliffs, New Jersey.

Scheme 1. The speaker writes down the points he wants to cover, lists the sub-points under each, writes his report from that outline or uses his list of points as notes. Don't use too many points. The audience can remember only so many. List the points in the best order for presentation, perhaps the weakest point first, the next strongest second, the big one last. Explain the points in terms of what they mean to the audience. Stress benefits, not points.

Scheme 2. Arrange the material under these headings:
  (1) What it is.
  (2) What it does.
  (3) What it means to the audience.
  (4) What the audience should do about it.

By filling in all the details involved in the answers to the questions, the speaker comes up with a workable scheme. The speaker can number his sections as he talks. For instance, "First, you'll be interested in what this scheme is; second, in what it does; third, in what it means to you; fourth, in what you should do about it." Use of the numbers gives the audience the idea that the speaker has organized his thoughts and knows what he is talking about.

Scheme 3. This scheme is simple to follow. The speaker arranges his material under these headings:
  (1) Yesterday
  (2) Today
  (3) Tomorrow

Scheme 4. This is the proverbial plan of the Negro preacher who had so much success in drawing crowds to hear him preach. When asked the secret of his success, he said, "First, I tells 'em what I'se going to tell 'em. Second, I tells 'em. And third, I tells 'em what I done tole 'em."

Scheme 5. When the speaker's objective is persuasion, use a sales formula:
  (1) Attract attention
  (2) Arouse interest
  (3) Create desire
  (4) Ask for action

Teachers of oral reporting suggest, "Begin with a startling statement that attracts attention." If a speaker starts with, "I'm going
to show you how to make money," he can be sure of attracting the
audience's attention. The speaker will have active attention if he
asks for a show of hands of those who wish to make money. Then
the speaker adds interest: "not a little money, a lot of money, more
than any of you dreamed was possible to make." So the speaker has
attention and interest. Now he can bring on the "benefit-to-you
story." The speaker tells why the audience should buy this plan,
what it will mean to them if they do. Then he winds up by suggesting what to do about it, sign the pledge card, write the congressman, etc. The speaker explains specifically what to do and exactly
how to do it.

Scheme 6. The speaker can use this scheme when he has con-
troversy.
  (1) Introduction
  (2) Advantages—Disadvantages
  (3) Conclusion

The speaker may be for or against the subject, but by listing the
talking points on the opposition's side, he gives the appearance of
being fair. Often the points in the speaker's favor stand up better
than if he had covered his side only. To work up a speech using this
scheme, the speaker takes a sheet of paper, draws a line down the
center: Advantages/Disadvantages. He can handle the subject in
two ways: (1) by listing all negatives, then all positives, or (2) by
listing a negative then a positive. If the speaker is on one side of
the question, he should list his side last.

These are the six basic schemes experienced speakers generally
use.

The organization and contents of a technical talk are, in general,
similar to those of the written report, although a certain degree of
flexibility is permissible for the purpose of increasing clarity or of
maintaining interest. Thoroughness, completeness, and rigor may
have to be sacrificed in order not to present the audience with more
than it can assimilate. Emphasis will be on no more than a very few
topics, and all the incidental material that would be meticulously

detailed in a written report will be largely eliminated from the talking report.

For example, if the speaker's experimental results and their implications form the essence of his talk, he should minimize the description and justification of his experimental technique. Here, of course, his language and manner are especially important. While curtailing his remarks on experimental techniques, he must give his audience a feeling of reasonable confidence in his results.

Technical talks frequently seem to be organized around slides or other visual material. The talks seem to consist only of descriptions and discussions of the slides, and even the introduction and the conclusions may depend on slides. There is no objection to such a presentation, so long as the speaker gets his message across. The audience must not conclude from such talks, however, that the slides were prepared first and the talk composed around them. Slides and charts should be composed along with the talk, not before it. A speaker should avoid preparing visuals first and then trying to decide what to say about them, because a considerable loss of smoothness and logic may result.

Time

Because program time is limited, organizing and writing an oral presentation can be even more demanding than for a manuscript that the speaker will publish in a scientific or engineering journal. Members of an audience cannot concentrate on a speaker's talk as they can on the paper read at leisure in relative seclusion. Neither can they go back and ponder a thought or an idea that is not at once crystal clear. Thus, it is essential to plan the talk carefully step by step, and to coordinate it properly with slides or other visual aids. The speaker should be able to describe his work in any specified amount of time, be it one minute or one hour, and all that is required of him is that he present as informative and understandable a story as possible within the allotted time.

Delivery

Engineers and scientists attending a meeting of any kind come to acquire information. Certainly, they enjoy a relevant humorous story that sets a scene or illustrates a point. But what the average scientist and engineer seeks are concrete, usable facts. He wants to share in the speaker's experience so he can broaden his own knowledge of the subject. In almost every case the engineer or scientist comes to listen and learn. Therefore the speaker begins with a sympathetic audience.

If the speaker considers that his audience may be hearing about eight to twelve talks during the day, on a variety of subjects in perhaps only a few of which he is expert, and if the speaker will ask himself how much a person can hope to learn in one day (learn, so that he will remember it for a long time), the speaker will see the futility of trying to cram detailed information into him as if stuffing a goose. The speaker's real mission will usually be successfully accomplished if he leaves the audience with a fairly clear impression of the nature of his work and of his most significant results or contributions.

Humor

On the other hand, if the audience is made up of students, salesmen, club members, or the like, a little more humor is desirable. If the speaker tells a joke on himself he should act as if he enjoyed telling it. When he says the first words he ought to have a smile on his face to indicate what is coming. When he gets off the point-making line, he can laugh with the audience. He must not laugh ahead of time, but join in the fun. The audience is having a good time, so the speaker should show that he is too.

If the speaker is trying to sell ideas he should not bury the ideas in humor. Those laughs he gets are like strong liquor. They go to his head and as the laughs come he forgets what he is trying to sell and concentrates on getting more laughs. He proves that he is a humorous speaker, but the idea he came to sell may be lost in the uproar. A little humor livens the speech designed to sell ideas, but the speaker must remember the main objective. Sell the idea; use the humor to hold interest. A speaker should remember that he does not need humor to make a good talk.

Enthusiasm

Never be ashamed to let enthusiasm show. Enthusiasm shows the speaker's sense of conviction about his subject. Enthusiasm and conviction build confidence in his audience. His ideas will be much more willingly accepted.

The speaker should show his enthusiasm and sincerity. If he wants people to pay attention to him, he should look directly at the audience—not over or through it, but directly at it. Warming up to the audience will help overcome feelings of self-consciousness on the speaker's part; it also helps the audience to be more comfortable. The speaker shows zest and enthusiasm and the audience responds to him. This establishes a friendly relationship with the audience.

Good speakers don't "speak at"—they "talk with." They strive to get ideas across and to convey useful information. That is what makes good conversation interesting. Lack of it makes many a talk extremely dull.

Suppose in conversation with a friend or casual acquaintance the speaker looks down when he says, "My wife is blond." By moving his head, looking down, and speaking softly he could give the impression that he is saying, "My wife is blind." The words *blind* and *blond* are similar; in careless speech they might not be clearly distinguished.

A speaker's sincerity can often make up for shortcomings in his technique. As former President Harry S. Truman has said, "Sincerity, honesty, and a direct manner are more important than special talent or personal polish in speaking."

Language and Style

Speak clearly and loudly enough so all can hear. If there is a microphone, speak directly into it, and try to stay the same distance from it throughout the talk. If the speaker turns his head to look at a slide, he should move the microphone so his voice does not fade. He should never make any remarks that cannot be heard by everyone in the audience. If he does, the audience will become confused and inattentive.

Use simple sentences, short words, and active verbs. Use terms the audience can readily understand. An informal, conversational style is best with personal pronouns (I, we) where appropriate. A speaker should express his ideas in the listener's language. The listener understands this best. Do not use professional jargon, unless the audience is familiar with it. The speaker must express his ideas clearly and accurately. He must remember that it is his ideas that the listeners will carry away. They will value his ideas far more highly than any momentary impression the speaker may make with humorous remarks or complicated gestures. Of course, these do help emphasize the speaker's remarks, but they should be kept at a minimum. A technical speaker ought to emphasize new products, new ideas, tools, savings, efficiencies, benefits, and advantages to his audience. A speaker keeps in mind that the audience is there to learn how his ideas can help them.

S. Katzoff from the National Aeronautic and Space Administration, Langley Research Center asks in his booklet "Clarity in Technical Reporting":

"If a friend or colleague should ask you to tell him about your research would you proceed with language of the following type?

" 'The momentum method of measuring profile drag, which consists of making total-pressure and static-pressure measurements across the wake and inserting these measurements into certain integral expressions developed by Betz and Jones, has been an important addition to experimental aerodynamics. Unfortunately, application to flight evaluation of the drag contributed by wing surface roughness or by various protuberances has been hampered by the experimental difficulty of making the necessary number of simultaneous pressure measurements in the wake.

" 'In the present research, an effort has been made to reduce the experimental complication in order that application to flight testing may be made more practical. . . .' "

Such sentences might well be used in the introduction of a printed technical report; but as a technical talk they demand a degree of concentration that most listeners cannot maintain. If, in addition, they are spoken in a rapid monotone, the audience will not follow the meaning and will be restless, almost from the very beginning.

Actually, as a result of years of experience in conversation, both technical and nontechnical, most people have developed a speaking style that is not too demanding of the listeners' mental processes, and that serves satisfactorily to convey ideas; and this speaking style, in general, is entirely different from that of a printed technical report. Using this style, a lecturer should speak to his friends or colleagues perhaps as follows:

"You're probably familiar with the momentum method of measuring profile drag (a pause, while you look at him to see whether he nods his head or merely looks blank; you decide to add a few words of explanation), in which you measure total and static pressures at a number of points across the wake, put the readings into certain formulas, and finally integrate across the wake to get the drag (a pause)—the profile drag, that is. The method ought to be especially useful for flight measurements behind actual airplane wings, in order to determine the drag due to (a pause, a slight motion of the hand, while you think of examples) rivet heads, gun ports, or any other irregularities. Now, trying to make all those measurements in the wake would require rather complicated instrumentation—which is the reason that it hasn't been done—and what I have tried to do is to simplify the method—especially to simplify the instrumentation—down to something more practical. . . ."

Language and mannerisms (pauses, hand motions, and so on) are more characteristic of some people than of others. A speaker's own normal manner of speaking, for example, may be entirely different from the previous speaker or the one to follow. Yet there is no objection at all to his having and expressing his own personality; and it is suggested that speakers do not try to imitate anyone else's mannerisms or style of speech.

In general, merely reading or reciting a carefully written technical report does not constitute a technical talk. In a scientist's daily technical discussions with his co-workers, or in teaching a class, he would not expect his friends or students to understand him if he poured forth such formal language—especially if he spoke rapidly and with an expressionless voice; and he should not demand more of an audience at a technical conference.

Speak Naturally

The technical talk is not merely a technical report that is short enough to read or recite in about twenty minutes; rather, it is a monologue, presented in whatever conversational, or perhaps teaching, manner is natural to the speaker, in which he tries his very best to get across a few basic ideas to his audience. Since the people in an audience cannot reexamine any sentence or paragraph that they find confusing, the speaker must make every thought clear enough to be understood the first time. If the thought is a difficult one, the speaker may find it best to repeat it, either in the identical words, or in different words and with a slightly different approach. For example, he might say "Perhaps you didn't quite follow that idea. What I mean is that if. . . ."

Speak easily and not too rapidly. Even an awkward hesitation, while the speaker gropes for the right word (just as in normal conversation), may have some value in that it excites the interest of the audience while it tries sympathetically to guess the word the speaker wants. The speaker should avoid affecting excessive casualness or extemporaneousness, since the effectiveness of his talk can be spoiled by the appearance of carelessness in its preparation or lack of earnestness in its presentation.

Pauses

Pauses are to give importance. Good talks need to be framed in silence by using the pause. Words and ideas need time to sink in.

Many speakers fill needed pauses with "static" and do not realize how much it interferes with meaning and attention. For instance, "Gentlemen: We . . . uh . . . are . . . er . . . faced . . . er . . . with a . . . huh . . . crisis."

And a misplaced pause can chop up even the best ideas into a jig-saw puzzle. The speaker can make use of the pause—after a unit of thought. A nonfunctional pause pattern such as: "I am happy . . . to . . . be . . . here . . . this . . . evening . . . on this . . . the . . . twenty-fifth . . . annual . . . celebration . . . of . . . the . . . founding," makes for a boring talk and loses audience attention waiting for the speaker "to drop the other shoe." Words are links which become a chain of thought only when they are joined together in phrases.

The speaker can change the rhythm, pace, and pitch. He can use variations in rhythm and timing to make a talk expressive and interesting. He can figure out and mark the parts that get the most stress—the rest of his talk should go more quickly. Then he can change the pace of his phrases and vary the pitch of his voice, according to the meaning and feeling. A talk should flow smoothly and logically from topic to topic; promise something beyond; avoid side issues. The few who want the details can read the paper when published.

Speaking Version of a Report

When an author of a good paper wishes to present that paper out loud he has two choices. First, he can *read* the paper. Second, he can give it from memory, using suitable notes to guide his thought.

Reading a paper is almost certain to kill interest and put the audience to sleep. If the speaker wants to talk to convey information to his audience, he can use, instead of his written report, a speaking version of his paper.

The speaker can write the speaking version. It is much shorter than the original written report, because speaking time is limited by a program schedule. Also it is much shorter because the audience cannot absorb all the details which are in the original. Limit the speaking version to the key points of the paper. Don't write the speaking version in sentence form, but use clauses and phrases; then there is less chance of reading the speaking version. If the speaking version is typed on 3 x 5-in. cards the speaker will appear to be speaking from notes, not from a full manuscript. If the speaker carries the cards with him for several days and reads them in spare moments he will get to know the words and thoughts he will present. It is best not to memorize the data on the cards. The speaker will require only occasional glances at the cards. And having the whole story at hand, on cards, does wonders for his confidence. Since the notes were prepared to sound like his conversation, an aside here and there during the presentation can create the illusion of an extemporaneous talk that is well organized.

If the speaker cannot use cards for his notes, and must read his paper, he should try to "talk" the written word. The speaking version of his paper should be highly legible copy, double or triple spaced, prepared with large-size type. The sheets ought to be numbered, unencumbered by clips or staples, so that each page lies flat and free for easy turning. The text ought to be placed on the rostrum in a manner that permits the speaker to look at his audience easily. He should not give the appearance of hiding behind the rostrum or the microphone.

Talk the written word slowly and clearly. The presentation should sound spontaneous, by varying the pitch of voice, length of pauses, pace, intensity, emphasis, and by looking directly at the audience.

Some experienced engineers and scientists who have presented a number of papers prefer to underline important sections of their paper in colored pencil, instead of using cards, or the speaking-version manuscript. These underlined sentences serve as a topic outline. While this scheme is fine for experienced speakers, it is dangerous for novices, because many beginners get stage fright. Then, instead of using the underlined sentences as an outline they read the entire text. Their voice deteriorates to a hushed monotone and the audience sleeps. So the new speaker will play safe and write out file cards for his first few speeches. Once he has enough experience he can switch to the underlining method if he wishes.

Rehearsal

There is no substitute for rehearsal aloud, with slides or other prepared visuals. The speaker can try it before a group of associates to get helpful criticism. Listening to a recording of his talk while viewing the slides is a good way to detect where improvements are needed. Either method will help the speaker to prevent faltering and monotony, and to keep within the allotted program time. Courtesy to the audience and other speakers dictates that his talk be made to fit within this time, allowing for some floor discussion.

Stage Fright

Perhaps it is the danger of stage fright that makes a speaker want to rely on written copy. Actually, much less reason exists for emotional reactions in technical talks than in typical college public speaking. In the latter, emphasis is generally on demonstrating or exhibiting the speaker himself, the contents of his speech being of secondary significance, whereas in the technical talk the contents are of paramount importance, and the speaker is merely the medium through which they are presented.

If the speaker listens to the comments of an audience after a technical conference has adjourned, he will find that oddities of presentation such as strange accents, speech defects, nervousness, or even grotesque eccentricities of manner seem to go virtually unnoticed so long as they do not interfere with intelligibility, and bitter criticism is applied only to speakers who read incomprehensible papers.

The speaker should bear in mind, then, that he is not required to give a polished performance, but only a clear one. His audience is not interested in judging *him*: they want only to understand what he is telling them.

Visual Aids

It is important for the speaker to remember that his talk should resemble as closely as possible the description of his work that he might give to one of his colleagues or fellow scientists. Just as he might show a friend a piece of apparatus, or go to the blackboard and make an explanatory sketch, so should the speaker use the same or similar visual aids in his talk. Instead of being shown on paper or on the blackboard, his illustrative material will normally be on charts or slides, prepared in advance with all necessary accuracy, clarity, and neatness. Do not consider, however, that such previous preparation saves much time in the presentation, or that the speaker may present a chart with nothing more than a vague gesture and remark like "This chart illustrates what I have just said," or "This picture speaks for itself."

A speaker should not plan on using every illustration in his published paper as a slide for his oral presentation. Instead he should choose a few key illustrations that demonstrate the main conclusions of his paper.

Color slides are becoming more popular every year. The color helps tell a better story and keeps audiences alert. If a speaker decides to use color slides, he can try to alternate them with a few black-and-white slides. This contrasts the two types of illustration and keeps the audience more interested.

Actually, a speaker's charts and slides often form the backbone of his talk, and each must be presented with utmost effort at clarity. State the subject of the slide, explain the units of the abscissa and ordinate; explain, if necessary, the special significance of the method of plotting, and, if the origin is not at the juncture of the scales, mention that fact also. Run the pointer along each curve as it is described, and tap sharply with the pointer at any point on the curve which needs special attention. (Avoid vigorously rubbing or gouging the projection screen with the pointer, as the glass-bead surface is easily damaged.)

The language a speaker uses while discussing his slides should be appropriate to his use of the pointer. For example, say "This top curve shows..." rather than "The upper curve of Figure 5 shows..." or "You can see in this equation that this term cancels this term and this term cancels this term," rather than "It may be seen in Equation (4) that the third and fourth terms on the left side are canceled by the second and fourth terms, respectively, on the right side."

The speaker must make every effort to keep charts and slides simple. It has already been emphasized that his purpose is to impart a few basic ideas rather than to present large quantities of information.

The number of slides and charts to prepare depends, of course, on many factors and can hardly be prescribed by formula. However, it may be of interest that experienced speakers seem to use about one slide for every two or three minutes of their talks. Presumably,

if a speaker uses fewer slides, he may be needlessly sacrificing helpful illustrative material, or else he may be trying to crowd too much
on each slide, while if he uses more slides he may be trying to present too much information. "Two to three minutes per slide," is
hardly a rule to be followed strictly; it is mentioned only as a guide
to help inexperienced technical speakers. The only rule that is absolutely basic is that the speaker's material be presented as clearly
as possible.

The principles a speaker ought to remember when planning slides
are:

(1) Each slide should present only one idea.

(2) The simpler the slide is, the better.

(3) Color may be used to advantage.

(4) The average presentation time per slide should be about two
to three minutes.

(5) Slides should be easily readable and drawn with quite heavy
curves and lettering. An indecipherable slide is worse than none
at all.

Technical and scientific societies have pamphlets on preparing
and presenting slides, or a speaker can refer to a library for a book
giving this information. Two pamphlets which are easily available
and give very useful information, including rules for size of lettering in making slides are: "A Guide for Preparing Technical Illustrations for Publication and Projection," prepared by the American
Society of Mechanical Engineers, and "Suggestions on How to Organize, Present, and Illustrate a Technical Paper," American Chemical Society, Washington 6, D.C., Bulletin 8, 1961.

A fine little book on oral communication and use of visual aids is
"Oral Communication of Technical Information" (Robert S. Casey,
Reinhold Pub. Corp., New York), and another is "Visual Art for
Industry," by George Magnan (same publisher).

Eastman Kodak Company has several easily available pamphlets which are highly recommended to anyone interested in technical reporting out loud and audio-visual aids: "Foundation for
Effective Audio-Visual Projection," Pamphlet No. S-3, "Art-Work
Size Standards for Projected Visuals," Pamphlet No. S-12, "Legibility Standards for Projected Material," Pamphlet No. S-4.

CHAPTER 16 *The Report Flood*

Scientists have been reporting their findings for over a hundred and fifty years so that others may read of their research and thereby share one another's work in order to promote scientific research and also to build reputations for themselves in an ethical manner.

It was not until the Second World War, though, and more particularly toward the end of that war, that the report became a major concern of all scientists. Prior to that time writing up one's research was largely a volunteer effort. The technical man had something to say and wished others to know of his accomplishments.

With the large emphasis of government-sponsored research during the Second World War the writing that a scientist did was somewhat less than voluntary. It became necessary with far-flung programs tied together toward a common objective that many men working on related subjects be kept informed as currently as possible about what the others were doing. The fact that much of this work was directed toward the production of electronically activated machines of one sort or another gave birth to the manual writing profession.

These comments should not be construed to imply that there were not reports written prior to the Second World War nor that there were no instruction manuals before that time. It was rather a question of volume. There were probably as many reports written during the years of the war as had been written altogether in the past. This probably also holds for instruction manuals. The wide diversity of equipment invented during the war had to be serviced, had to be operated, had to be repaired, and the need for these manuals became nearly an emergency. In a very real sense, report writing was born, as a major concern of most scientists and other technical people, about the time of the Second World War.

It was shortly thereafter that it became quite apparent to those who made a practice of reading these reports that skill in technical writing was something which most technical people had not been taught. Over the years books had been written on how to write reports. Papers on this subject appeared in most technical journals. Specialists toured the country to teach people how to write better, and courses were gradually introduced into universities at the advanced undergraduate and graduate levels to teach students how best to convey the results of their research and development.

As more and more people gained skill or had the responsibility for writing, more and more reports were generated. As we look back on the flood of words which is gradually threatening to engulf us, it is not uncommon today to hear of the information explosion, which refers to the continued exponential growth of the number of pages of reports which have come from the nation's technical laboratories. This flood of documents created a problem and a profession of its own.

The traditional librarians found themselves inadequate to cope with this inundation of paper. Their traditional manuscript was a book. These new materials called reports were in some respects not books. These were very important respects. First of all, the subject matter was extremely narrow; the number of copies in existence was limited; in most cases they were soft cover and would not stand up on the shelves; titles were long; authors were either multiple or non-existent. In many cases the only authorship that could be really identified was the institution which issued the document.

These reports just didn't fit the librarian's classical techniques. According to the scientific tradition, therefore, new techniques began to appear to fill the vacuum created by this new method of communication. New and different kinds of indexing methods became important and became practiced in the larger report libraries. Where there were large report collections in the same installation with computers, it became obvious that computers could assist in handling the indexing problem of the report literature.

The computer here, however, was nothing but a tool to assist the librarian in the tremendous volume of clerical work necessary to keep current with the flood of reports. Considerable work was done and indeed is still going on to determine the best methods of performing the intellectual work involved in indexing reports of narrow subject matter.

Terms like *shallow indexing* and *deep indexing, word lists* and *thesauri, autoindexing* and *autoabstracting* became significant to those who had become skilled in handling the new report literature. These people dug and probed and indexed and read and reread these reports. They tried successfully or vainly to answer questions about them from their indexes and thereby became proficient in the technique of the storage and retrieval of technical information to produce documents in reply to requests.

Finally a few people suggested that it might be more efficient if one were to store this technical information before it became a document. This intriguing thought has caused a number of experiments to be conducted in both industrial and governmental laboratories to determine whether all this writing was necessary to maintain the cooperative scientific programs widely scattered about the country. It was necessary for those who were doing this progressive thinking to limit themselves to areas which were largely under their control. Therefore, it is not surprising that this idea of the storage and retrieval of information prior to the existence of a document has not received wide publicity, except among the enthusiasts themselves. Their publications have appeared in their own special journals, such as *American Documentation, The Journal of Chemical Documentation, Special Libraries, etc.*

It is interesting to note the antagonistic reaction that occurred among the report-writing scientists toward this new idea. Previously there had been much hue and cry about the stiff requirements in writing reports, against the number of reports required, about the many times the same words were said in different ways for different audiences, and from librarians and authors who had to handle or read the large volume of reports. It was these same people who immediately raised objection to the idea that perhaps reports did not, after all, have to be written by people in order to communicate their laboratory findings. Those who complained the loudest about their writing chore objected most strongly when offered a possible solution.

The fundamental principles of this heresy assume, without too much experimental evidence, the following caveats:

(1) Scientists do not like to write.

(2) The physical problem of indexing and storing reports is rapidly becoming unmanageable.

(3) The intellectual and economic problems of indexing a large volume of reports has not yet been solved satisfactorily.

(4) Most scientists are spending about half of their time communicating, and it would be a major contribution to the economy of the country if this percentage could be appreciably reduced.

(5) There are a large number of errors in these reports which crept into them through the technique of repetitious copying.

(6) There is a strong feeling that there is knowledge stored in these reports that is largely unretrievable because of the geometry of its storage; either the retrieval lists were produced under clumsy headings or the accumulation of the information was mechanically inconvenient.

On the basis of these caveats it was determined in several installations to attempt to employ mechanical and electronic storing techniques based entirely upon data stored in notebooks.

Experiments were begun at several pharmaceutical houses. The National Institutes of Health * and at least one chemical company, Monsanto,† described how raw data were transcribed to some mechanical storage device, such as a punch card, or magnetic tape, or a 3 x 5 cord, or microfilm, or what have you. For example, in the Monsanto case, a specially designed notebook was used by the

---

* Leiter, J., Schneiderman, M., and Miller, E., "Data Processing Program of the Cancer Chemotherapy National Service Center, Utilizing the IBM 305 (RAMAC)," presented at the 136th Meeting of the Am. Chem. Soc., Div. Chem. Lit., Atlantic City, N.J., Sept. 13-18, 1959.

† Waldo, W. H. and DeBacker, M., "Printing Chemical Structures Electronically: Encoded Compounds Searched Generically with IBM-702," presented before the International Conference on Scientific Information, Wash. D.C., Fall, 1958; Waldo, W. H., Gordon, R. S., and Porter, J. D., "Routine Report Writing by Computer," *Am. Doc.* 9(1), 28 (1958).

laboratory people, so that IBM keypunch operators could punch directly from the notebook onto cards. The data were then fed to a computer which reorganized the data in such a way as to print out a report for distribution without any handwriting being done.

The IBM Company is developing this technique for use internally for the preparation and editing of instruction manuals by computer, thereby reducing the effort and embarrassing time lag between the development of improved hardware and the issuance of manuals for maintenance, repair, and operation.

This description is grossly oversimplified, but it does represent the history and the principles involved in a new revolution in report writing currently taking place. As these experiments become more widely known and techniques more widely accepted, it is entirely conceivable that the great majority of laboratory experimentation may be stored directly into machines throughout the country, permitting the report writers and the journals to concern themselves with discussion and interpretation more and more and with the repetition of experimental data less and less. It is to this end that the next chapters are devoted.

CHAPTER 17   *Modern Reporting Requires Modern Thinking*

Mankind is learning things so fast that it's a problem how to store information so it can be found when needed. Not finding it costs the U.S. over $1 billion a year. Now machines are being called on for help.

From: Bello, F., "How to Cope with Information," *Fortune*, Sept., 1960, pp. 162-192.

Much sooner than most of us expect, massive changes will occur in report writing.

Today technical communication is composed of reports, manuals, proposals, journals, books, symposia, conversations, and a host of lesser techniques like letter writing, local section and national meetings of technical societies, seminars. These classical methods have served science well for many generations. In recent years, however, a number of additional techniques have become available for communicating technical information faster and more accurately. These new techniques are known as *modern methods of handling technical information.*

Some of these techniques involve microfilm, peek-a-boo cards, Uniterms, notations, and computers. Unfortunately for the author, most of these new techniques are for purposes of retrieving information.

The pioneering work done by Calvin Mooers and his "descripters," of Mortimer Taube, head of Documentation Inc., James W.

Perry, with his telegraphic abstract, and Hans Peter Luhn, "the Father of Information Retrieval," have led to massive improvements in the retrieval of references, documents, and information extracted from a store of documents. Only a modest advance has been made in improving the means by which documents are created.

The use of modern methods of creating documents is progressing slowly with the recognition by authors that much of what they write could perhaps be done better by machine. The hesitancy to accept this fact stems from the understandable fear that machines are challenging the right of the author to express himself in his own way.

Most scientists and engineers are individualists and they want nothing to interfere with their freedom to think, conclude, and recommend on the basis of their own findings and professional judgment.

No computer is likely to infringe this right in the foreseeable future. But there are modern methods of creating documents that can be used to assist these scientists in pursuing their individual freedom. However, long entrenched habits are difficult to alter. Modern methods of handling technical information are and will continue to be inhibited in their growth by the unwillingness of the present generation of scientists and engineers to change established procedure.

This inhibition appears unfortunate, even pathetic, to the observer. The so-called *invisible college,* for instance, represents a highly emotional resistance to the inevitable. These colleges came about spontaneously, apparently as a protective measure to withstand the flood of papers in the more highly popular disciplines. There are such colleges in the field of electronics, organic chemistry, medicine, molecular biology, applied mathematics, and indeed the study of the storage and retrieval of technique information itself.

Many workers seek in these fields to gain reputations for excellence by submitting many papers for publication and delivery at technical meetings. Quite unconsciously in some cases, and with more deliberateness in others, leaders in these fields have tended to accept a certain few "qualified" workers and to reject others as outsiders. Those who are "in" constitute the "invisible college" and readily share the fruits of their work with one another. They referee one another's papers with little or no criticism because they have already discussed them during previous face-to-face visits at conferences, whose attendance was by invitation. The officers of the societies are passed around this circle. Reputations are cooperatively enhanced.

This description of present day "invisible colleges" is neither an indictment nor an indorsement. It is mentioned as a symptom of a muddy interface between the old and the new. The new is arriving somewhat faster than the means of assimilation can digest it.

The new began with the punch card, but no one in the scientific professions believed it would ever disrupt the classical methods of technical communication. The punch card was accepted with enthusiasm as a tool for accountants and as a means for solving enormous arithmetic problems hitherto impossible because of their size. It was unthinkable, though, that it would have any direct influence on the highly personal art of report writing. Research departments in industry, "invisible colleges" in the scientific disciplines, the members of the classical sciences and engineers were too busy defending their projects from what they believed to be the more violent influences threatening their sanctity such as, technical competition, budgets, and politics.

An example of the difficulty of assimilating the new methods of communicating into classical science made the newspaper headlines when the first weather satellites were placed in orbit. The satellites were able to take more pictures of the earth's weather than was possible to evaluate in time to take advantage of the information.

The expanded growth of new technical journals to the point where no scientist had the time to keep abreast of his own burgeoning specialty has become upsetting. The influence of the invention of more electronic instruments than the bench man could master; of the rapid obsolescence of technical knowledge; and of the gross cross-disciplinary effects being reported has generated a defensive attitude among individual scientists throughout the world.

Scientists have not yet noticed that the solution to this massive feedback of the results of science upon the individual scientist depends on two things. These are simple to describe and seem naive when first contemplated. They will, indeed, relieve some of the pressures influencing the thinking of many scientists.

The first solution is a commodity that is relatively available to science today—money. The second is less easily obtainable: the willingness of individual scientists to humble themselves before the massive knowledge accumulated during the past two decades.

The individual technical man has not comprehended the awesome magnitude of the data available to him in his own area of specialty. He has heard of the flood of information. He knows others are concerned, but he is not conscious of what he is missing to help him solve his own laboratory problems.

The leaders of today's science remember vividly the total recall that their university mentor appeared to have when these leaders were in school. They desire earnestly to be able to impress their colleagues and juniors in the same way. They have not accepted the fact that, regardless of the discipline, there is at least four times as much known today. They do not yet believe it is impossible to speak with the assurance of their predecessor a generation ago.

Given the humility to face the staggering facts and a reasonably large amount of long-term money, science and engineering can again be in control of its growth through the use of the punch card and its younger brothers, magnetic tape and core memories.

The application of the punch card in the library is being generally ignored by the practicing scientist and engineer. It is of little concern to them how librarians answer literature questions so long as they continue to do so. People who work in libraries have the poorest image of all the devotees of science. As a result, much of what has been accomplished with punch cards in the past decade is unappreciated by the scientific community at large.

Libraries are being automated at a rapid rate. The use of the punch card, from sorter to computer, and the use of microfilm and photocopier has begun to change the very appearance of the library. As a major customer of the technical journals, librarians have influenced the origin of daringly different journals such as *BASIC* and *Chemical Titles,* both produced entirely by computer and other automatic equipment.

At least one journal is available today on microcards, another on magnetic tape, and *Chemical Abstracts,* the world's largest and most influential abstract journal in science, began to offer its services on microfilm in 1965. The Joint Engineering Council annoyed most engineers by asking them to submit indexing terms together with their papers for publication to facilitate installation of modern methods of handling technical information. The National Library of Medicine in its MEDLARS project will be handling, for one of the world's largest scientific disciplines, a larger volume of published literature than any mechanized system in existence. Ironically, the mechanization is all in the retrieval function to solve library problems.

During the past ten years an amazing thing has happened. Librarians have quietly developed techniques and know-how to solve the difficult problems of coping with this new mass of specialized technical information. They have independently solved the problems of literature retrieval, but have had little to do with information storage.

When the "invisible colleges" face up to the long-term impossibility of continued discrimination against their growing numbers of competent scientific competitors, and begin to integrate all the knowledge mankind has accumulated, the public image of science will be much improved. Willingness to adapt some modern library techniques to their report writing will be an important step.

The money problem is a little different from problems that scientists are used to handling. Corporations, government sponsors, foundations, and educational institutions will discover that they are being asked to invest large amounts of risk capital for the storage and retrieval of technical information, whereas previously they maintained a library or information center with an eye toward minimum cost rather than maximum return. Because this return on investment is difficult to measure, very little has been invested in very large-scale technical information systems. We must learn to treat information as a commodity. Today it is largely unpriced. In time, buying and selling this commodity through a mechanized retrieval system may keep many brokerages in business.

A description of the means of handling the outpouring of technical information at some time in the future will be changed, and might go somewhat like this:

A daily newspaper recording the newest in the world of science will routinely be found on the desks of each scientist and engineer throughout the country each morning as he reports for work. It will have been printed in the nearby computer room through a remote control hookup from the central information store operating as a result of preprogrammed questions put to a learning machine which was being continuously updated by the outpourings of the laboratories of the world the previous day.

An item of potential commercial interest, or of importance to national security, developed in these laboratories will have patents automatically issued, and security classifications automatically assigned. Manufacturing facilities will have been drastically altered to take advantage of the very rapid obsolescence and innovation. Fortunes will be made and lost on the fluctuations in the bid and asked prices of information as well as that of grain or copper. The success of business ventures will depend more upon knowing how to ask the right question than upon making the right decision.

To ask the right question has been recognized as the most critical problem in our growing field of mechanized report writing. The problem is not new; it is as old as organized scientific research. The significance of asking proper questions will take on new importance. When much of the data taking is automated, when the data are stored mechanically and reports are written by computer, when retrieval of information is only a clerical problem, the significance of a scientist being able to foresee the question that needs to be asked and being able to ask it unambiguously will be recognized as the ultimate intellectual effort required of the learned.

The increased pace of research and engineering and the continued shortage of trained scientists able to imagine, think, and plan effectively will soon force the introduction of modern methods of handling technical information into more and more of mankind's laboratories, and ultimately into all kinds of report writing.

CHAPTER 18   *Technical Report Writing by Computer*

Determining whether the techniques of modern methods for the storage and retrieval of technical data can be applied to a given research program requires a candid and objective view of the nature of the research being carried out. Few laboratory people like to admit that their work is routine. If, however, there is a repetitive aspect to the manner in which laboratory work is being conducted, modern methods may be directly applicable.

There are only a few chemical laboratories or engineering laboratories of a bench scale that do not engage in some form of testing. It matters not whether the testing procedures are frequently changed; it matters only that the method be described once in classical report form and given a designation.

The observations taken according to these prescribed testing techniques, whether they be words or numbers or letters, are amenable to the modern methods of data storage.

Techniques have been described in many of the scientific fields for the application of this new technique to report writing. During the planning and installation of such a new system a few principles must be kept uppermost in mind.

(1) The cooperation of the investigators must be obtained.

(2) The purpose of the endeavor must be to minimize the time spent by the investigator storing and retrieving the information once it is obtained.

(3) Although all possible mechanical methods should be examined for the storage and retrieval of this information, one must

always be aware of the necessity for leaving the investigator in charge. The machine is a tool, not a master.

(4) All systems should be devised so that revision is permitted, the easier the better.

(5) The output of the system must be "hard copy" and in such a form as to be readily interpreted by those not familiar with the intricacies of the manner in which the data are taken and stored.

(6) The system should permit faster reporting of the information than by classical methods.

(7) It should not be anticipated that the system will save money in the short run. There are many justifications for the installation of such a system in appropriate locations. One of them, however, is not reduction of the annual budget.

Investigator Cooperation

The investigator whose report writing is to be automated must understand that none of his scientific prerogatives are to be withdrawn. He is to be given a new and powerful tool. He is not to be made the slave of a machine. He should be asked to cooperate in an experiment in the sociology of science and not be made the pawn of systems planners. His knowledge, experience, and judgment should be requested and respected. He should be given a money-back guarantee that if the system does not achieve the promised relief, he will be welcome to return to his classical report-writing ways. Without the support of the data taker, automated report writing is doomed to the boneyard of good ideas that didn't work.

Time Saving

The major purpose of the venture is to maximize the value of the scientist and engineer. Even though the number of skilled scientists leaving school each year is rapidly increasing, there will never be enough to justify wasting their talents on archaic techniques. Giving skilled people the tools to make them more productive is different from "pampering" scientists and placing them on pedestals. One of the products of research is information. The warehousing, retrieval, and marketing of this information should be as efficient as its generation. Modern methods of handling technical information should save time.

The Scientist and His Tool

Clever systems designers know that there are cybernetic techniques to wrest control from the scientist once he records his observations. Application of such techniques in the design of routine report writing procedures must be scrupulously avoided. The individual scientist or engineer must continue to be responsible for his work. Conclusions, recommendations, and plans for future work is a human skill requiring a subjectivity and understanding no machine begins to simulate today. Report writing systems, manual or automatic, must always be subject to the direct influence of the scientific acumen of the data taker. If the system helps the man be more efficient and productive, it should be made available to him as a tool for his use.

Revisions

Only the most conservative laboratories resist an improvement in test procedures. The institution of an expensive, rigid, automatic data-handling system, fixed field, hardware-bound, will inhibit the institution of new data-gathering methods. When this occurs, the machine is controlling the research and should be scrapped. Programming flexibility is a prerequisite to report-writing systems design. Provision should be made for new test techniques, improved measurement accuracy, additional parameters, new retrieval requirements, while still maintaining the viability of the old data.

Output

Have empathy for the reader even though the report is mechanically produced! Poor format is doing more to instill antagonism to computer-produced documents than any other one factor. Long lists of close-spaced all-capital letters are most forbidding. More white space, different type fonts, and upper and lower case letters is a step in the right direction, but not enough.

English translation of machine codes must appear in the hard copy. Odd abbreviations should be spelled out, units of measure should be clear, and conditions of test should be clearly understood or described.

Computer designers have a penchant for odd-shaped paper. Reports should be distributed on 8½ x 11 or 8 x 10 in. paper whenever possible. Furthermore, the sheets should be separated and bound in a conventional manner. The computer is as much a tool for the reader as for the writer.

The reader should not be forced to change his habits to satisfy the desires of the systems designer or to lend convenience to the hardware people.

Speed

There have been many computer installations where the total time from data gathering to ultimate user was lengthened even though the actual computer operations may have taken only moments. This result should not be permitted in the processing of technical information. There must be a net saving in the report processing time, or the system may be self-defeating. Time can be lost when batching of reports is required. The ultimate is an on-line, real-time system. A balance should be achieved between speed required and cost.

Cost

True cost/performance ratio can only be determined when a dollar value (not cost) can be placed on the information handled. Since this cannot normally be done, the cost of such a system must be justified on technical man-hours saved, faster and more accurate reporting. The cost of systems design, programming, computer operation, and data storage, when depreciated over several years, will pay dividends through previously impossible data correlations and a study of long-term trends. However, the annual cost of report writing will inevitably increase.

Report writing by computer is a special case of using modern methods for the storage and retrieval of technical information. It is special in two respects. In one respect the information involved is raw data obtained without further treatment by the investigator. In the case of the laboratory scientist, the raw data are meter readings and other observations. The non-experimental scientist accumulates his data from surveys, calculations, etc. and submits them to the report-writing system without editing.

The storage of raw data is important because a large part of the bias imposed by data evaluation is eliminated at the input stage. If there are several occasions in the future when evaluation seems in order, the raw data are always there. Most of the effort in modern studies of the storage and retrieval of technical information deals with already evaluated information: the report literature or the journal literature. Report writing by computer is a special case because it deals with unevaluated, raw data.

It is a special case in another respect. Computerized report writing is so new that the cases in existence are relatively unknown, whereas the storage and retrieval of evaluated information by modern methods has been going on for a decade; an industry has grown up around the concept; millionaries have already emerged from the business.

Pioneering work of the late Hans Peter Luhn, while he was with IBM, highlighted possibilities of indexing and abstracting the report wholly by computer. The key-word-in-context index, finding more and more devotees today, is a direct outgrowth of Luhn's thinking about the use of machines to facilitate the early communication of technical information from source to user. The basis for this work is the assumption that the words most aptly describing the subject matter will occur rather frequently in the report. Thus the computer is taught to determine the frequency of every word in the report. Those words which occur most frequently, such as *and, but, the, is,* etc. are automatically eliminated. The remaining most frequent words become the center of attention for the computer. The machine reproduces a set number of sentences that contain these words, and prints them out under the heading: *Abstract*.

It is claimed that this technique produces a mighty poor abstract. To a degree the criticism is valid, but it is *uniformly* mediocre, whereas man-made abstracts range from useless to excellent.

Computer programs for writing reports, manuals, or abstracts are not readily available. They are being used, however, in many organizations. They are not available because they are not excellent programs. They are beginnings. In certain cases they also are being held proprietary because, even in their crude form, they have been tremendous successes and are giving these companies competitive advantage over the less automated technical organizations.

As machines take over more and more of the mechanical parts of report writing, it becomes increasingly important that technical authors give more attention to the creative sections. The sections devoted to experimental or project plan and objectives, conclusions, and recommendations require the best brains mankind can develop. This brain power should not be wasted copying data in tables, rewriting experimental procedures, and proofreading this material when it is typewritten, type-set, and made up in pages.

For the skeptics who read this, there is reproduced below a news item taken, with permission, from the December 21, 1964 issue of *Chemical and Engineering News,* page 76.

Flacks Losing Work to Computer

The following item appeared in "The Washington Post" for Dec. 8 under the byline of Susanna McBee:

"In the beginning, the executive who wanted publicity would call on the reporters and tell them the news.

"It came to pass, however, that he no longer had time to tell the news himself. And he hired public relations men, or flacks, as they later were called.

"Soon the flacks saw that they did not have the time to write all the stories that the executive wanted. They yearned for a wondrous machine that would bring forth the routine news and leave them time for creative efforts.

"Lo, last week the U.S. Census Bureau discovered it has an electronic computer that begets press releases and addresses them.

"Hallelujah, said the flacks, as they beheld the first compositions of the machine. These news releases told all the people of 1963 retail trade figures for counties in Idaho and Montana.

"Most Census Bureau flacks were filled with joy. They wrote a 26-line news release about the computer's 22-line release.

"A few of the flacks and all of the press, it is said, were sorely jealous over the grace, the style, the wit of the computer's release, which began:

Bannock County's 493 establishments had $73.0 million in sales in 1963, an increase of 21 per cent from 1958, the U.S. Bureau of the Census has just reported after tabulating data gathered from all firms in the 1963 census of business.

"And it shall come to pass within the next few months that the look-no-hands releases will have multiplied exceedingly. Blessed will be the 16,000 news outlets in the Nation's 3000 counties, for they shall have received these releases."

APPENDIX A *Abbreviations*

The following list of technical abbreviations is printed here (with permission) from the latest edition of the *Style Manual* compiled by the American Institute of Physics.

When a long word or phrase is needed frequently in an article, it may be replaced by an abbreviation that is explained when it first occurs, for example, molecular orbital (MO). The abbreviations in the list below are so common that they may be used without explanation. No periods are used except in special cases noted. Abbreviations of units are written in the same way for the singular and the plural. Abbreviations of units and the symbol for percent (%) are used only when preceded by a numeral.

absolute ampere	abamp	average	av
alternating current	ac	bar	spell out
altitude	alt	barn	b
ampere	A	billion electron volts	BeV
ampere-hour	A-h	biot	Bi
ampere-turn per meter	At/m	body-centered cubic	bcc
angstrom	Å	boiling point	bp
anno Domini	A.D.	British thermal units	Btu
ante meridiem	a.m.	calculated	calc
antilogarithm	antilog	calorie	cal
aperture ratio 16	f/16	Calorie	Cal
approximate	approx	candela	cd
atmosphere, standard	A_s	candlepower	cp
atmospheres	atm	candles per square meter	c/m^2
atomic mass units	amu	Celsius	C
atomic weight	at. wt	centimeter	cm
audio-frequency (adj.)	af	center of mass	c.m.

257

centimeter-gram-second	cgs	face-centered cubic	fcc
centipoise	cP	farad	F
Chapter	Chap.	fermi ($= 10^{-13}$ cm)	F
chemically pure	cp	Figure	Fig.
coefficient	coeff	foot	ft
cologarithm	colog	foot-candle	ft-c
constant	const	foot-lambert	ft-L
contact potential		foot-pound	ft-lb
difference	cpd	franklin	Fr
continuous wave	cw	frequency modulation	FM
cosecant	csc	gallon	gal
cosine	cos	gauss	G
cotangent	cot	gilbert	Gi
coulomb	C	gram	g
counts per second	counts/sec	henry	H
cubic	cu	hertz (cycle per second)	Hz
cubic centimeter	cc or cm³	hexagonal close packed	hcp
curie	Ci	horsepower	hp
cycle	spell out	hour	h
cycles per second	cps	hyperbolic cosecant	csch
debye	D	hyperbolic cosine	cosh
decibel	dB	hyperbolic cotangent	coth
degree	deg	hyperbolic sine	sinh
degrees Baumé	°B	hyperfine structure	hfs
degrees Celsius		inch	in.
(centigrade)	°C	inside diameter	i.d.
degrees Fahrenheit	°F	intermediate frequency	i.f.
degrees Kelvin		international angstrom	IÅ
(absolute)	°K	International Critical	
diameter	diam	Tables	ICT
direct current	dc	joule	J
disintegrations per second	dis/sec	kaiser	K
dyne	dyn	kilocalorie	kcal
east	E	kilocycle/second	kc/sec
electromagnetic units	emu	kiloelectron volt	keV
electromotive force	emf	kilogauss	kG
electron volts	eV	kilogram	kg
electrostatic units	esu	kilogram-meter	kg-m
entropy unit	eu	kilogram-weight	kg-wt
equation	Eq.	kilohm	kΩ
equations	Eqs.	kilojoule	kJ
erg	spell out	kiloliter	kl
exponential	exp	kilometer	km
exponential integral	Ei	kilo-oersted	kOe

kilovolt	kV	million volts	MV
kilovolt-ampere	kVA	millivolts	mV
kilowatt	kW	minimum	min
kilowatt-hour	kWh	minute	min
kinetic energy	KE	molar	M
laboratory	lab	mole	spell out
lambert	L	nanosecond	nsec
latitude	lat	neper	Np
limit	lim	newton	N
liter	spell out	north	N
logarithm	log	nuclear magneton	nm
logarithm, natural	ln	number	No.
lumen	lm	observed	obs
lumens per watt	lm/W	oersted	Oe
lux	lx	ohm	Ω
magnetomotive force	mmf	ounce	oz
maximum	max	outside diameter	o.d.
maxwell	Mx	page	p.
megacycle/second	Mc/sec	pages	pp.
megohm	$M\Omega$	picofarad	pF
melting point	mp	poise	P
meter	m	post meridiem	p.m.
meter-kilogram-second	mks	potential difference	PD
microampere	μA	pound	lb
microangstrom	$\mu\text{\AA}$	pounds per square inch	psi
microcoulomb	μC	probable error	pe
microfarad	μF	radian	rad
micromicrofarad	$\mu\mu F$	radio-frequency (adj.)	rf
micromole	μM	revolutions per minute	rpm
micron	μ	roentgen	R
microsecond	μsec	root mean square	rms
mile	spell out	ryberg	Ry
miles per hour	mph	secant	sec
milliampere	mA	second	sec
millibarn	mb	section	Sec.
millicurie	mCi	sine	sin
milligram	mg	south	S
millihenry	mH	square	sq
milliliter	ml	standard temperature	
milli-mass-units	mmu	and pressure	STP
millimeter	mm	steradian	sr
millimicron	$m\mu$	tangent	tan
millimole	mM	tesla (Wb/m²)	T
million electron volts	MeV	ultrahigh frequency	uhf

ultraviolet	uv	watt	W
versus	vs	weber	Wb
volt	V	weight	wt
volume (measure)	vol	west	W
Volume (book)	Vol.	x units	xu

The common biochemical abbreviations are taken from Chemical Abstracts Service, "Directions for Abstractors," Ohio State University, Columbus, Ohio 43210, 1964 pp. 7-1 to 7-4.

adrenocorticotropin	ACTH
adenosine 5'-diphosphate	ADP
adenosine 5'-monophosphate	AMP
adenosine 5'-triphosphate	ATP
adenosinetriphosphatase	ATPase
cytidine 5'-diphosphate	CDP
carboxymethyl cellulose	CM-cellulose
cytidine 5'-monophosphate	CMP
coenzyme A	CoA
cytidine 5'-triphosphate	CTP
diethylaminoethyl cellulose	DEAE-cellulose
deoxyribonucleic acid	DNA
deoxyribonuclease	DNase
dephosphopyridine nucleotide (NAD)	DPN
reduced DPN	DPNH
flavine adenine dinucleotide	FAD
flavine mononucleotide	FMN
follicle-stimulating	FSH
guanosine 5'-diphosphate	GDP
guanosine 5'-monophosphate	GMP
guanosine 5'-triphosphate	GTP
inosine 5'-diphosphate	IDP
inosine 5'-monophosphate	IMP
inosine 5'-triphosphate	ITP
interstitial cell-stimulating hormone	ICSH
luteinizing hormone	LH
melanocyte-stimulating hormone	MSH
nicotinamide adenine dinucleotide (DPN)	NAD
reduced NAD	NADH
nicotinamide adenine dinucleotide phosphate (TPN)	NADP
reduced NADP	NADPH
nicotinamide mononucleotide	NMN

ribonucleic acid	RNA
ribonuclease	RNase
triethylaminoethyl cellulose	TEAE-cellulose
triphosphopyridine nucleotide (NADP)	TPN
reduced TPN	TPNH
tris(hydroxymethyl)aminomethane	Tris
thyroid-stimulating hormone	TSH
uridine 5'-diphosphate	UDP
uridine 5'-monophosphate	UMP
uridine 5'-triphosphate	UTP

alanine	Ala	isoleucine	Ile
argine	Arg	leucine	Leu
asparagine	Asn	lysine	Lys
aspartic acid	Asp	methionine	Met
cystine (half)	Cys or Cys	ornithine	Orn
cysteine	Cys	phenylalanine	Phe
glutamic acid	Glu	proline	Pro
glutamine	Gln	serine	Ser
glycine	Gly	threonine	Thr
histidine	His	tryptophan	Try
hydroxylysine	Hyl	tyrosine	Tyr
hydroxyproline	Hyp	valine	Val

Tables and Figures

The examples used here for good reporting of tables and figures were taken from: "Preparation of Technical Reports and Papers," by McMahon, E. M., Bridwell, R. S., Cassell, G. S., and West, M., Tennessee Eastman Co., Research Laboratories, Kingsport, Tenn., Sept., 1962.

The reference number (superscript [61]) used with Figure 1 is for illustration only.

TABLE I

Effectiveness of Phenolic Compounds as Antioxidants for Cellulose Acetate Butyrate [a]

Additive	Apparent Oxygen Absorbed, Ml	Degradation of Mol Wt, %	Ref
None	35	49	48, 49
Phenyl salicylate	44	40	50
Phenyl m-hydroxybenzoate	25	33	51
Phenyl p-hydroxybenzoate	24	27	52
Catechol monobenzoate	16	42	53
Resorcinol monobenzoate	8	8	54
Hydroquinone monobenzoate	0	0	55

[a] 1g cellulose ester in 25 ml dibutyl sebacate heated 2 hr at 150°C with 0.02 g additive under oxygen

TABLE II

Military Specifications for Jet Engine Lubricants

Property	Specification			
	Mil-L-7808 D[6]	Mil-L-25336[7]	Mil-L-9236 A[3]	Proposed Mil-L-9236[8,9]
Composition	Unlimited	Unlimited	Unlimited	
Appearance	Clear, uniform	Clear, uniform	Clear, uniform	
Viscosity, cs				
At −65°F	Max 13,000	Max 13,000	Report	
At 100°F	Min 11.0	Min 11.0	Report	Min 11.0
At 210°F	Min 3.0	Min 3.0	Min 3.0	Min 3.0
At 400°F	—	—	Report temp. in °F for 13,000 cs	Min 1.0
Other			—	
Viscosity stability at −65°F, cs				
3-Hr test, % allowable variation from original viscosity	Max ± 6% but <13,000	Max ± 3% but <13,000	Report	
72-Hr test	Max <17,000	Max <13,000		Max 21,000
Pour point, °F	Max −75	Max −75		Max −75
Flash point (Cleveland open cup), °F	Min 400	Min 400	Min 500	Min 400
Spontaneous ignition temp., °F			Report	Min 750
Evapn wt loss (6.5 hr at 400°F), %	Max 35	Max 35	Max 5	Max 15
Foaming characteristics, ml-ml-sec				
Sequence I, 75°F	100-0-5	100-0-5	100-0-5	
Sequence II, 200°F	25-0-3	25-0-3	25-0-3	
Sequence III, 75°F	100-0-5	100-0-5	100-0-5	
Load-carrying ability (Ryder Gear), lb	68% of ref. "B" (min 8 tests)	Min 2,800	Min 2,800	Report
Compatibility with other approved oils	Pass	Pass		Mil-O-6081, Mil-L-7808, Mil-L-25336 oils
Effect on synthetic rubber, % swell	Min 12 Max 35	Min 12 Max 35		Under development
Panel coke				
Mg at 600°F	Max 80	Max 80		
Mg at 700°F			Max 100	
Oxidation-corrosion stability in air	72 Hr at 347°F	72 Hr at 347°F	48 Hr at 500°F	425°F till a break in viscosity change vs. time curve
Wt change of catalysts, mg/sq cm				
Cu	± 0.4	± 0.4	± 0.4	Fe ± 0.2
Mg, Fe, Al, Ag	± 0.2	± 0.2	± 0.2	
Ti	—	—	± 0.2	
	No pitting or etching	No pitting or etching	No pitting, etching, or deposits	No pitting, etching, or heavy deposits

263

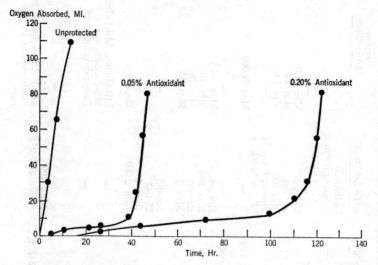

FIGURE 1. Effect of antioxidant concentration on absorption of oxygen by polyethylene.[61]

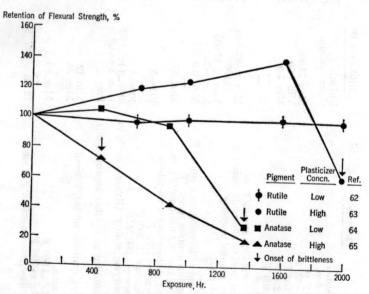

FIGURE 2. Weathering resistance of pigmented plasticized and stabilized cellulose ester.

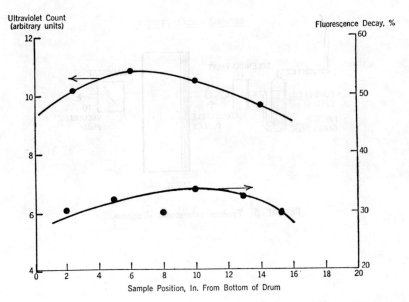

FIGURE 3. Effect of sample position on illumination received in unmodified weather-ometer.

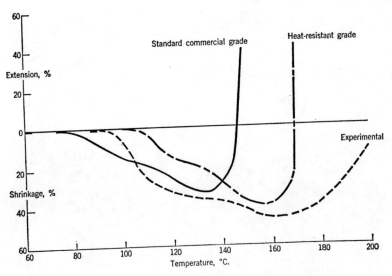

FIGURE 4. Thermal behavior of some methacrylate resins.

APPENDIX B

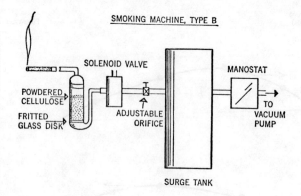

SMOKING MACHINE, TYPE B

POWDERED CELLULOSE

FRITTED GLASS DISK

SOLENOID VALVE

ADJUSTABLE ORIFICE

MANOSTAT

TO VACUUM PUMP

SURGE TANK

FIGURE 5. Typical schematic diagram.

APPENDIX C *Compound Words*

The tendency in scientific spelling is to avoid the hyphen when it does not serve a useful purpose. Words which formerly were hyphenated have now become either one word or two words in many instances (for example; setup, cross section). It is correct to hyphenate adjectival combinations or words, as in the phrase "beta-ray spectrum." The rule is sometimes relaxed when there is no risk of ambiguity. A list of words common in technical writing and scientific journals with preferred spellings is printed here as a help to the technical report writer. For nonscientific words "Webster" is the authority.

air-cooled
airtight
afterward
asbestos-covered (adj.)
audio frequency (noun)
ballpoint
bandwidth
bedplate
belt-driven
blowdown
blowoff
blueprint
boilerhouse
boiling point
bottleneck
boxboard
buildup
built-in

burnout
bypass
byproduct
camshaft
cathode ray
chain-driven (adj.)
cloud chamber
coenzyme
cold-rolled
countercurrent
co-worker
crank-driven (adj.)
crankshaft
cross section
cutback
cutoff
cutout
dewpoint

die-cast
diecasting
diesel-driven
diesel-electric
direct-connected
direct-current
disk-shaped
double-duty
downcomer
downdraft
downstream
downtime
drainpipe
drivescrew
drive shaft
drive wheel
dry cell
dry ice

dry kiln
electron volt
end point
engine-driven (adj.)
eyepiece
fast-moving (adj.)
feedback
feed value
fiberboard
fingertip
firebrick
fire clay
fire-resistant
firsthand (adj.)
five-ply
flameproof
flange nut
flashover
flashproof
flowmeter
forearm
fourfold
frostproof
gas-fired
gas-heated
gasholder
gas-laden
gas main
gastight
gearbox
gearcase
gear-driven (adj.)
gear-operated
goldleaf
gold-plated
halfway
half-hour
half-life
half width
heat-resistant
heat-treating
high-pressure (adj.)
horsepower
hot-rolled (adj.)

ill-assorted
infrared
kiln-dry
kilovolt-ampere
kilowatt-hour
knife edge
knife switch
knockout
know-how
lap-welded
lead-covered
locknut
lockwasher
loudspeaker
low-pressure (adj.)
made-over
make-up
makeup (noun)
man-hour
manpower
metal-clad
metal-coated
metal-lined
metalworker
microbiological
microwave
midyear
midpoint
monomolecular
motor-driven
multicolor
multirecord
nickel-plated
nickelplate (verb)
nonradioactive
offcenter
oilcup
oil-driven
oilhole
oil-temper
oiltight
on-and-off (noun, adj.)
one-half
out-of-date (adj.)

ovendried
overall (adv.)
over-all (adj.)
overheat
packing box
panelboard
para state
papermaker
paper pulp
part-time (adj.)
penholder
penpoint
percent
percentage
phase-wound (adj.)
photomicrograph
phototube
pickup
pig iron
pipefitter
pipeline
pound-foot
power-driven
powerhouse
powerline
power-operated
printwheel
profitmaking
public-minded (adj.)
public-spirited
pugmill
pulldown (noun, adj.)
pull-push (adj.)
pulpwood
pumphouse
punchcard
pushbutton
push-pull
quick-freeze (verb, adj.)
quick-freezing (adj.)
radioactive
radio frequency
rainproof
ram-jet

razoredge
razoredged
reabsorb
re-educate
re-enter
reexamine
repairman
rest mass
right-angle (adj.)
right-angled (adj.)
right hand
right-handed (adj.)
rubber-lined
rustproof
rust-resistant
sandpaper
scrap heap
scrap iron
screwdown (adj.)
screw-driven (adj.)
screwdriver
screwhead
seamweld (verb)
seam-welded
semisolid
serviceman
servomechanism
servomotor
setscrew
setup
shakedown (noun, adj.)
shatterproof
shearpin
shock-resistant
short circuit
short-circuited
short-lived
shunt-wound
shutdown
shutoff
silverplate (verb)
silver-plated (adj.)
silver-plating
single-edged

single-phase
sixfold
slide rule
slide valve
slipring
slip-up (noun, adj.)
small-scale
smoke-filled
smokehouse
smokestack
snap-acting (adj.)
somebody
someday
somehow
someone (anyone)
some one (distributive)
someplace
something
sometime (adv., adj.)
some time (some time ago)
sometimes
someway
somewhat
somewhere
sound-absorbing
soundproof
spark coil
sparkover (noun, adj.)
spark plug
spindle-formed
splashproof
splinterproof
split-level
split second
spot check
spot-checked
spotlight
spotweld
spot-welded
spot-welding
sprayroom
spray-washed
spring lock
spur-driven

square-bottomed
square foot
square root
standby (noun, adj.)
standpipe
standpoint
star wheel
starchmaker
starchmaking
startup (noun, adj.)
staybar
staybolt
steambath
steam boiler
steam-cooked
steam-driven
steamfitter
steam heat
steampipe
steampiping
steam-propelled
steamtight
steam turbine
steel-cased
steelclad
steelmaker
steelmaking
steelwork
steelworker
steelyard
stepdown (noun, adj.)
step-up (noun, adj.)
stopcock
storeroom
stovehouse
straightedge
straight-edged
straightforward
straight-up
strap-shaped
sugar-coat (verb)
sugar-coated
sugar-cured
switchboard

switchbox
switchgear
switchplate
switchplug
tankhouse
teardown (noun, adj.)
tear-off
tear-out (noun, adj.)
testhouse
testroom
thought-provoking
thoughtworthy
three-dimensional
three-ply
throughput
thumbscrew
tight-fitting
tile-clad
tinfoil
tin-lined
tin-plated
tin-plating
trouble-free
troubleproof
turndown (noun, adj.)
twofold
two-piece
two-ply
ultrahigh
U-shaped
U-tube
un-ionized (adj.)
unseal
V-shaped

valve gear
vapor bath
vapor-filled
vaportight
venthole
viewpoint
volt-ampere
voltmeter
waist-high
water-cool (verb)
water-cooled
water-filled
water-free
water jacket
water level
waterline
waterpower
water pressure
waterproof
waterproofed
water-soaked
water-soluble
watertight
water tower
watt-hour
wattmeter
waveform
wavelength
wax-coated
wax paper
weatherproof
wedge-shaped
weekday
weekend

weighthouse
well-informed
well-known
wet bulb
wide-angle
widemouthed
wide-open (adj.)
widespread
wingnut
wire cloth
wire edge
wire-edged
wire gage
wire recorder
wire rope
wire-wound
wood-paneled
woodpulp
woodbox
work force
worndown (adj.)
wornout
worthwhile (noun, adj.)
wristpin
writeup (noun, adj.)
wrought iron
x axis
x direction
x ray (but, to x-ray)
y axis
Y potential
zinc-coated
zinc blend

Index

Abbreviations, 58, 86, 97, 100, 105, 109, 112-114, 253
  for scientific and engineering terms, 112
Abstract, 40, 52, 255
  indicative, 40
  informative, 40
Acknowledgments, 53
Adverbs, 148, 149
Alliteration, 126
Ambiguity, 25
American Chemical Society, 112
American Institute of Physics, 58
Analysis, 2, 20
Analytical results, 103
Anaphora, 156
Antecedents, 121-125
Apostrophe, 92, 93
Apothecary units, 62
Appendix, 47, 53, 107, 206
Approval, 218
Aristotle, 12
Art work, 216
Astrophysical Journal, 43
Atomic weight, 102
Authority list, 55
Authors, 37, 73
Automated data taking, 249

BASIC, 247
Bias, 4, 159, 254
Bibliography, 16

Binding, 33
Biological Abstracts, 43
Board of Geographic Names, 93
Body, 45
Boiler plate, 207
Boldface, 108
Books, 72
Braces, 99
Brackets, 86, 99
Brevity, 26, 198
Bulletins, tables-of-contents, 35

Cacophony, 191
Capitals, 109-111
Captions, 60
Cards
  edge-notched, 16
  file, 15
  punched, 16
Chemical Abstracts, 80, 82, 248
Chemical Abstracts Service, 35, 43, 76, 102, 113
  Directions for Abstractors, 114
Chemical Titles, 247
Chronological order, 62
Churchill, Sir Winston, 127
Clarity, 25, 100, 112, 120, 134, 155, 181, 197, 217
Classification, 55
Clauses, 88-90
Clichés, 130, 131
Coherence, 140

Honorarium, 15
Hyphen, 95-98

Ibid., 77, 78
Ideas, 143
Idem, 77, 79
Illustrations, 26, 112
Index, 54
Indexer, 35
Inferences, 4, 5
Infinitives
   dangling, 127
   split, 125, 126
Information retrieval, 249
Insincerity, 198
Inspiration, 15
Interlingua, 10
Interpretation, 157, 224
Interviews, 15
Introduction, 3, 44, 206, 224
Investigation, 224
Investigator cooperation, 251
Italics, 108, 109
IUPAC, 113

Jargon, 7, 100, 129, 130
Joint Engineering Council, 248
Journal, 13, 26, 71, 75, 84, 87, 99, 102, 246
   express, 30
   technical, 12
Journal of Negative Results, 209
Journal of the American Chemical Society, 102
Journal of the American Medical Association, 43, 112
Judgments, 4

Key-word-in-context index, 254
Key words, 16, 36, 217
Korzybski, Count Alfred, 179

Layout, 22
Laziness, 11

Legends, 87
Letter Symbols for Chemical Engineering, 112
Linguistics, 179
Linotype, 32
Literature search, 15
Litotes, 156
Loc. cit., 77, 78
Logical analysis, 128, 129
Luhn, Hans Peter, 245, 254

Magnetic tape, 248
Mannerisms, 232
Manual, 208
Manuscript, 25, 30
Market survey, 14
Materials, description of, 45
Mathematics, 84
Meaning, 160, 184, 185
   implied, 193
   multiple, 161-177
MEDLARS, 248
Metaphor, 156, 188
Metric units, 57
Microcards, 247
Microfilm, 83, 244
Misinformation, 5
Mixed units, 57
Modern methods, 244, 249, 250, 254
Modifiers, 118, 119
   misplaced, 193
Monologue, 233
Mooers, Calvin, 244
Multilith, 32

Narration, 216-218
Nomenclature, 158
Notations, 244
Notebook, 18
   references, 83
Note taking, 15
Nouns, collective, 124, 125
Numbers, 87, 103-105

14691

John Willard Brister
Library
Memphis State University
Memphis, Tennessee